# TALES FROM THE ROD ROOM

# TALES FROM THE ROD ROOM

## Michael Paulet

*Illustrations by Roni Wilkinson*

WHARNCLIFFE PUBLISHING LIMITED

First published in 1994 by
Wharncliffe Publishing Limited
47 Church Street, Barnsley,
South Yorkshire S70 2AS

A CIP catalogue record for this book is available from the British Library

ISBN 1 871647 22 3

For up-to-date information about other titles produced under the Wharncliffe
Publishing imprint, please telephone or write to:

Wharncliffe Publishing Limited
FREEPOST
47 Church Street
South Yorkshire S70 2BR

Telephone no. (24 hours): (0226) 734555

Typeset by Yorkshire Web, in Plantin 11 point

Printed by
Redwood Books,
Trowbridge, Wiltshire

# CONTENTS

GOD grant
That I may live to fish
Until my dying day
And when it comes to my last cast
I then most humbly pray
When in the Lord's safe-keeping net
I'm peacefully asleep
That in His mercy I be judged
As good enough to keep

# Chapter One

# The Stranger

The road, deep in the Highlands of Scotland, tries to follow the course of the river. It is the only course the road can follow without taking on the impossibly steep gradients of the mountains on either side of the strath. The traveller keeps the river in sight off and on for ten miles or so until the road degenerates into a stony track. Sometimes only a steep bank separates road and river, and sometimes they part company as the river twists and tumbles.

As I drive up or down this road my eyes constantly wander from road to river; the minds of fishermen like me are easily diverted to thoughts of those fellow travellers, the salmon. I know that road like the back of my hand – a danger in itself. I try not to become over-familiar with its twists and bumps which may hide a car, bicyclist, walker, or sheep, but where I can see along the straight, narrow stretch of tarmac with the grass growing through in places, I trundle along at reduced speed with alternate glances at road and river through windscreen and side-window. Occasionally there is an impatient peep from a car-horn behind me.

I note the height of the water as it runs over boulder-strewn stretches, cascades through deep granite channels, and tastes each pool with a tongue of current. I note the colour, from crystal clear to oloroso sherry, and occasionally to brown windsor soup as the burns scour when the spate comes. And where I can see them, I note the activities of the fishermen.

It was on a bright day in early summer that I drove down this road to Ardroy, the village which stands at the point where the river leaves the road for good and joins the Kyle, and the Kyle the Firth. Today the river was running at a nice height with a stain of peat in the water. On the way down the strath I saw a car with empty rodracks on the roof parked in the loop of a cart-track. I recognised it as belonging to Jock Robertson, who had the Cloonie stretch of the river. He'd have a fish or two on the bank by lunchtime, I guessed. Jock didn't mess around. He thought like a salmon and if there were fish to be caught he'd catch them.

Ardroy stands on one side of the Kyle, Bettybridge on the other. Neither village is remotely attractive; each a cluster of grey and white houses spreading untidily inland. The Kyle is spanned by an unspectacular metal cantilevered road bridge which joins the two villages. Beneath the bridge the swirling water is pushed backwards and forwards by the tide coming up the Firth and by the outflow of the four rivers coming down the Kyle. And with the tide come the salmon and sea trout. When the nets are on, some get no further than just above the metal road bridge. Here there is a rocky outcrop like some rough-hewn landing-stage; one or two cumbersome rowing boats are moored alongside, there is a rusty iron winch, a small hut, and lots of empty wooden fish-boxes piled untidily about. This is the netting station.

In spring and the earlier part of the summer, as the combined strength of the rivers begin to push back the tide, the netsmen row out from the jetty, two of them pulling hard on the oars, the third man paying out the net from the stern of the boat, to make a semi-circle of bobbing corks half way across the Kyle. The law forbids them from going more than

2

half-way across, so there is still some freeway for ascending salmon. They pull back to the jetty, hard work now dragging the net against the current, beach the boat, and attach the dragline of the net to the winch. Old and rusty it may be, but the winch still works well, and the noose of nylon netting closes in.

That morning I watched this process, as I often had, with a mixture of curiosity and annoyance that such a basic method should be used to scoop fresh-run salmon from the water like flabby cod. A kicking fish that had all the river to run lifted from the net, thumped on the head, and chucked, bright silver, to tarnish on the spit of rock before being piled in the boxes marked Kyle Fisheries. But if I was passing that way and the nets were on, I never could resist the temptation to watch. I did my errands in Bettybridge and drove home.

On the way back up the strath I noticed a maroon Volvo with empty rodracks parked in the gateway of a track leading down to the river. Strange, I thought to myself, I wonder who that is? I parked the car and walked down to investigate. As I got closer I recognised the scrawny figure of Alec Ross. Who on earth was the man with him, and what was he doing fishing here? What's more, it looked as if the stranger had a salmon at the end of his line. Alec was capable of many things, but ghillieing for poachers was not one of them. There had to be some explanation, and I would do better to bide my time, and hold my tongue, until I found out what it was.

Indeed, the man *had* got a fish. At one moment the rod bent in a taut arc, then I heard the sound of the ratchet of the reel at full revs, and saw the salmon jump thirty yards downstream.

There was a shout from Alec: 'For God's sake drop the point o' yer rod.'

Obviously today's disciple was not an experienced salmon fisherman, and, to judge by the flailing of Alec Ross's arms, communication between the two of them had not been established to Alec's satisfaction. For the time being the salmon remained attached to the fisherman's line. My impression was that Alec did not think this was a situation which would last much longer.

The salmon now charged the bank at the spot occupied by its two would-be captors. Alec's impassioned voice greeted this move. 'Reel up, reel up, mon, you dinna want to lasso the damned fush.'

Fortunately the salmon came to a stop directly below the bank, where it presumably reckoned it could put the granite undercut to good use. Once again, to judge by the straining arc of his rod, the fisherman regained contact. 'I think I've got him now, I can see him quite plain,' he exclaimed.

'Aye, so can I,' said Alec, 'he's fretting yer line against the rock. Back doon stream, will ye, and gie him the butt. If he breaks ye it'll be sooner rather than later.'

From the tone of voice I could guess what was going through Alec Ross's mind: he was cursing his fate of having to cope with idiots who lost fish because the rod was in their hands and not his. If the man couldn't do what he was told, he deserved to lose the salmon, and the sooner the better as it was getting on for lunchtime.

At least the first part of Alec's instructions had been understood by the fisherman, who was now stepping gingerly backwards, not giving an inch of line for the good reason that he had the handle of the reel firmly grasped between forefinger and thumb of his right hand. The second part, that of 'Gieing him the butt', hardly likely to be understood by many a more experienced angler, followed automatically.

Then I saw Alec unship the long wooden-handled gaff he carried strung across his back, and prostrate himself on the bank.

I could only guess what was happening. I was not close enough to see anything more than the straining rod, the line at a thirty-degree angle to the tip, the fisherman's back, and the soles of Alec Ross's boots. I imagine the salmon – it must be a smallish one – had been caught off balance and tugged by main force from its tactical position beneath the outcrop of rock. Before the fish had a chance to regain its equilibrium and fight on, Alec must have seen his chance.

There was a shout of 'Step roond me, dinna trip over me for God's sake. Keep tight hold, and keep walkin' backwards. If he hasna' broke ye by now he never will.' Then Alec struck with the gaff. The next moment a wriggling salmon was pitched clear on to the bank, and Alec Ross was struggling to his feet. He stood up, saw me, and said, 'I was aye handy wi' the gaff'. I had often suspected as much.

I said good morning to the fisherman. I don't know who he took me for, but he seemed in no way put out by my arrival on the scene. He returned the greeting, made some remark about it being his lucky day, then made off towards his fishing bag left some way upstream. 'Aye, lucky for some, unlucky for yon wee saumon,' Alec Ross observed to me as he watched the retreating back. 'There's fules in the water as well as oot o' it.'

'But who is he, Alec?' I asked. 'What's he doing here?'

'The mistress sent for me a while back, and asked me tae take 'im fushin'. His name's Sir Ernest Cartrell, or saethin' like that.'

'Well, if that's what my wife told you, you'd better carry on,' I said, and walked back to the car. I drove back a couple of miles up the strath; the little road jinked over a hump, split from a stony track, like the thicker fork of a stick, and entered the pine trees; it ambled on even bumpier now, and there on the left was the familiar drive. A sharp left turn, a steep gradient, over a girdered metal river bridge wide enough for one car only, and Balmeanie Lodge standing there white and turreted across a strip of rough grass euphemistically called the Park.

I parked the car in the yard surrounded by a small complex of slate-roofed buildings of various purpose: deer larder, old battery house from before Balmeanie came on mains electricity, garages, and ghillie's lodgings now unoccupied. Alec Ross's cottage was further down the brae, as they say in Scotland. I have yet to find out the exact definition of a brae, but I take it to be a big bank, and big bank there was at the back of Alec's cottage. I could see at the foot of it the usual two or three weakling lambs rescued by Mrs Ross from being knocked on the head, fed by her on the bottle, and now reluctant to leave home comforts for the rigours of the hill. There, too, in the small field in front, were the stirk and followers, a cow and her offspring which according to custom were entitled to free grazing.

I walked round to the glass-fronted porch which formed the entrance to the Lodge. In wet weather the shaggy stuffed wild goat's head which hung high up on the wall above the hats, coats, sticks and other paraphernalia gave off a musty smell. It was as good as a barometer. No smell today. I resisted the temptation to go outside again, and spent the afternoon catching up with the paperwork I ought to have dealt with long ago, put off day after day on the pretext that it could wait until tomorrow, as happens with many of life's more irksome chores during summer in the Highlands of Scotland.

Now I was looking forward to a drink, and dinner. I went downstairs. As I approached the drawing room, I heard a voice from the other side of the open door, a man's voice. I paused outside. The pitch of the voice resembled that of a salesman; there was a hint of the North Country to it. I had heard that voice before, quite recently. I listened.

'That fish hit my fly with a bang and shot across the river like a runaway train, the line slicing through the water after him. Then he jumped, but I was ready for him. I dropped the point of my rod in time and tightened again. Then he came straight at me. I reeled in for all I was worth, he was close in under my bank now. Then I really put the pressure on. That shifted 'im. Just as I was getting the fish under control, that ghillie chap, Alec Ross, shouting instructions I couldn't understand in his queer Scotch voice, made a dive with his gaff. Out comes the salmon before I've even had a chance to play 'im properly. I says to Ross what did you do that for? And he says, there's some fish that are damned unlucky and that were one of them. I don't know quite what he meant by that.'

I went in to the drawing room.

My wife got up from the sofa. 'Darling, this is Sir Ernest Cantrell', she said. The man, who had obviously not heard me enter the room, turned from where he had been standing, and as his eye met mine I could sense the uncertainty of his recognition — where have I seen this man before? he was saying to himself. He probed for the missing clue, 'Haven't you and I met somewhere before?' he queried.

'Yes,' I said, 'briefly this morning. You were fishing.'

When we went up to bed, my wife Ann said, 'Oh darling, I forgot to tell you this morning that Sir Ernest Cantrell would be arriving early.'

# Chapter Two

# Balmeanie

Would the builder of Balmeanie Lodge turn in his grave if he were to discover that the place was now being run on commercial lines? I doubt it. After all, he built the lodge on the fruits of trade, or more precisely on the profits he made before the turn of the century manufacturing a popular brand of sauce. Balmeanie may have been built for pleasure out of profit, but now pleasure has had to be turned back into profit to keep the place going. I am sure the old sauce-maker might have appreciated the irony of this; at least when he was working his way up through the ranks in commerce, before he purchased his promotion to Highland laird.

And I suspect that it was not just the Highland scenery and the opportunity for sport that caught the fancy of the builder of Balmeanie Lodge. There is nothing new in status symbols, though the ability to choose such a one as this, or, more imposingly, the red-brick Gothic castle he also built for himself a few miles further south, are out of today's price range for letting people know that you are seriously rich. The north of Scotland is dotted with such monuments to English commercial achievement; most are in glorious settings, a few in good taste, many in bad. The architecture follows more or less the same pattern: square blocks of granite masonry with round turrets at every available corner. The ultimate Victorian status symbol.

English industrialists with newly acquired wealth were not the only ones to proclaim their status in granite in the glens north of Inverness. Another local castle of quite hideous proportions was run up with a different motive in mind. Down on the Kyle about twelve miles from Balmeanie stands an example of Scottish Baronial architecture at its worst. It was built in the last century by a Scottish countess who fell out with her husband. She had this perpendicular pre-Disneyland castle constructed on a spur of rock overlooking the road which her husband must take on the way to his estates further north. It was to stand as a permanent reminder to him of her extravagance at his expense.

These monuments to the whim of wealth still look disconsolately out over the glens they no longer control. A hundred years ago or thereabouts they were built, their purpose is served, and they are redundant: one is a youth hostel, and the other stands forlorn and empty. Only one castle in the area is still a private home. It was once occupied by the old laird, but is now the home of an Arab plutocrat who has added a helicopter pad and a security fence. He travels up there occasionally with two chefs and a ten-man body-guard. The locals are not admitted to find out what other splendours have been wrought inside.

The lodges like Balmeanie, built at about the same time, are a more feasible proposition − with certain adjustments − for late-twentieth-century living for those of us not in the mega-rich bracket.

Balmeanie Lodge was bought in the 1960s by a would-be laird from London, a stockbroker who began accumulating money before the words 'Insider Dealing' gained the currency which they have today. He retired early and settled down to his second career as the proprietor of a Highland estate. But he kept in touch with his City contacts, and in due course arranged a convenient deal through the solicitor of one of his former clients, whereby the Balmeanie estate was sold (at a considerable profit, I later learnt) as a hedge against death duties to a rich old lady living in Bournemouth. He continued to live there on a lease-back arrangement. Shortly afterwards he had a stroke and died. The rich old lady living in Bournemouth was my maiden aunt. Quite unexpectedly she made Balmeanie over to me, on condition I went to live there.

My name, by the way, is Charles Rowley, and my wife's name is Ann. I chucked my job as an estate agent, sold — with some regret I admit — the house we had in Berkshire, and moved north, to take over an isolated lodge and ten thousand acres of peat, rough grass, heather and water.

Rough hill land in the north of Scotland supports only one domestic beast, the sheep. There is no cash crop to harvest each year. Trees may until recently have been a valuable long-term investment for absentee landlords, but occasional clumps of scots fir and silver birch hardly provide a regular cash-flow for a resident owner. Up to this point Balmeanie had always lived on unearned income; now I had to teach the place to earn its keep. The most evident asset of Balmeanie was the sporting potential of the place.

The obvious starting point was the fishing, and my wife and I decided to take in paying guests who, we hoped, would come to fish our stretch of the main river, the Struie, the smaller river (classified on the map as a burn) that feeds it, and the various hill lochs. Fishermen are on the whole easy guests; they seek solitude but mix well together. Besides, at Balmeanie I could fish alone to my heart's content, but I like the company of other fishermen with whom I can share today's experiences and discuss tomorrow's chances. If I cannot always afford to have my friends to fish for free, I find there is a freemasonry among fishermen which leaves friendship not far behind. The exchange of money, if sensibly arranged, need be no obstacle. Or so we thought, and we have largely been proved right.

Although there is deer-stalking and grouse shooting over dogs as well, we decided to treat these as separate operations, maybe letting the stalking on a longer-term lease and chucking the grouse shooting in as an extra with the late-season fishing.

I think at this point I should try to describe the Balmeanie estate — the house and the fishing, at any rate, because both are the catalysts for the stories that follow.

Balmeanie Lodge is far from being an architectural gem — few Highland lodges are — but it is a pleasant house of medium size; white-painted, slate-roofed, and with the mandatory turret on one corner of the four-square building. There is a veranda to command the breathtaking view up the strath, and a high wall to one side which protects a flower garden from the sheep and the deer that come in from the hill to pillage the plants. There is an extensive range of outbuildings — steadings, as they are called in Scotland — one white square tacked on another beneath a topiary of grey slate. If the cumulative effect does not enhance the natural beauty of the scenery, neither does it offend. It is neutral. Balmeanie Lodge was built for its owner, family and friends, to take their pleasure and to live in comfort amidst glorious scenery.

Inside Balmeanie welcomes you with well-proportioned rooms, cool in summer and warm in winter; an absence of dark passageways, imposingly high ceilings, antlers, panelling and tartan. It is a house to be lived in rather than a lodge to be stayed in. Even if the décor is a bit shabby in places, you feel the coat of fresh paint can wait just a little longer, the armchairs with the drooping seats comfortably fit the backside, there is a tarnished pane in the beautiful gilt-framed looking-glass over the drawing room fireplace, there is an infilling of paperbacks in the big Victorian bookcase in the hall, and the clock which hangs opposite with 'Highland Railway Company' on the face permanently strikes one stroke over the hour. As for the pictures on the walls — well, some of them are good; in particular there is a most delightful oil painting of a boy in the velvet and lace of Stuart times. He gazes wistfully down the length of the dining-room table, catching your glance wherever you happen to be sitting, and holding it for a moment whilst he asks you to consider his presence on the wall. The interior of Balmeanie Lodge glows with warmth, if it does not sparkle with elegance.

We came to the conclusion, my wife and I, that there had to be a further consideration, other than that of earning money, which would persuade us to share our home with people we did not know; we had to make as sure as we possibly could beforehand that they would be the sort of people we could get on with, or else the whole thing would not be worthwhile. We might just as well let the fishing, take the money, and let the fishermen look after themselves. In fact, by whatever means possible it would be our aim to attract like-minded people (so far as we could judge) as our guests, who might be expected to get on with one another and make up a contented house party. We did not flatter ourselves that we could always achieve this, but at least we could take the trouble to try. We would be acting as any good host and hostess should, choosing our guests carefully, and seeing as best we could that they got on together whilst they were with us. Not always easy, and not at all easy when your guests are paying for the privilege of staying with you. However, the fishing, and the atmosphere of Balmeanie, would do a great deal, it was up to us to do the rest.

For the purpose of the stories that follow it doesn't matter how we set about this task; it is enough to say that friends, business colleagues, and former clients (it was a help having been at the up-market end of the estate agent's business) put the word about for us, and we worked out a carefully considered mailing list with an equally carefully constructed personal letter to each person on it. We were very selective, preferring to reject the doubtful – with suitable excuses – rather than take a chance on a potentially tiresome guest; that we may have been wrong on occasions I do not doubt, but it seemed better to be safe than sorry when it came to our first priority, people who came to stay getting on with one another.

Of course, we made our mistakes, but as time went on we established a guest list from which we could offer a diminishing quantity of available dates for a booking, of not less than a fortnight's duration, throughout the fishing season. In most cases we began to know the returning faces, the habits, and the foibles of our guests, and to look forward with few exceptions to their arrival each season.

A word now about the fishing at Balmeanie. It falls

12

conveniently into three beats: the main river – the Struie – above the Lodge, the Struie below the Lodge, and the Balmeanie Burn. The best of the fishing is above the Lodge where, beginning with the Falls O'Meanie pool, the river has carved its course through the solid granite, falling pool by pool – there are five of them – over a distance of about half a mile. Below the Lodge, the Struie gradually widens itself as the river becomes less constricted in its course, and the solid granite walls give way to grass banks from which you can wade out a little over the bed of serrated rock to fish the less dramatic pools formed by the outcrops. Half-way down, under a steep rock cliff, the Balmeanie Burn, insignificant except when in spate, joins the main river. The pools downstream from the Lodge generally hold fewer salmon, especially in the spring when the fish are in a hurry to push upstream, moving unhindered until they reach the Falls O' Meanie.

The Falls O' Meanie pool is the end of journey for ascending salmon. They get no further. The river, wide enough above, is suddenly forced by the rock into a narrow ravine down which the full force of the current plunges, pauses in a turbulent cauldron, and plunges again – a drop of perhaps some eighteen feet in all. The cauldron half-way down has worn away the rock to form a deep pot where the water swirls and the ascending fish pause to recover from the first stage of their battle with the pent-up force of water. Few, if any, salmon ever achieve the second stage of the ascent: up and out of the pot, through the next cascade and into the quiet stream above. They are knocked off course by a cross-current and fall back exhausted, slapping and floundering against the slippery rock wall into the depths of the Falls O' Meanie pool.

The irony is that above this natural fault there is a long line of rocky linns by which salmon could easily ascend to the wide green strath beyond. Here, buried in the hills, the current flows gently, joined by the burns which feed it, meandering over gravel beds, losing itself altogether in dark mysterious pools. The perfect spawning-ground for salmon.

13

We are still arguing with other riparian interests about a fish-pass at the Falls O' Meanie.

When we came to Balmeanie we had two sitting tenants: Jim Fraser the shepherd, and Alec Ross the ghillie-cum-handyman. We have since added a cook, Mrs McKenzie, and her eighteen-year-old daughter Flora; Mrs Ross (Alec's wife) also comes into the house to help out. The female contingent come under the jurisdiction of my wife Ann, and I direct the activities of the male staff. When the occasion demands, Jim Fraser doubles up as a ghillie. Then Alec Ross will proudly introduce himself to whoever he is accompanying that day as the head ghillie.

I have learnt a lot about the Scottish ghillie since I came north; sometimes he is taciturn to the point of rudeness, sometimes he is talkative, sometimes he is not half as well-informed as he would have you believe. I have listened to a newly engaged ghillie holding forth on what fly to use and how to fish it, knowing that he has spent the previous ten years as a keeper-stalker on a deer forest where there is nothing larger than an overgrown burn to fish with a worm for six-inch trout.

The experienced ghillie, like many of field sports' supporting cast who depend on tips as part of their income, is seldom over-optimistic, whatever he thinks of your chances. Today, when there are training courses for almost any occupation, I often wonder what the curriculum would be if a ghillie's course were to be organised. Certainly there would be a period devoted to psychology, under the heading perhaps of 'Getting to know your gentleman' (I suppose the man with the money wielding the rod is still so classified in the ghillie's mind). One of the first lessons to be learnt under this heading: cast doubt on the chances of your gentleman successfully landing a fish, then when he does so, success will be well rewarded.

A ghillie, mentor to all manner of fishers during the course of a season, soon learns to be a realist. Around these parts there is a retired policeman who ghillies when he is wanted (and I suspect poaches when he is not); as a result he knows the river like the back of his hand. His name is Kenny Forbes. The beat below Balmeanie is let on a time-share basis; I happened to be at the end of our water there when I saw a man I did not know fishing the pool below with Kenny in attendance. I wandered down to see if they had had any luck. I rather doubted it, because it was early in the season and there were not many fish up. As I approached I heard a crack each time the man cast. 'Kenny,' I said quietly, 'it's none of my business and I hope you don't think I'm interfering, but it doesn't sound as if your man has got a fly on his cast.'

'Indeed he has not,' said Kenny. 'He's from Tanganicker, he's had me up the trees all morning freein' his fly. He's better off wi'out one. There's nae fish in the river anyhow.' I left the unsuspecting fisherman from Tanzania and Kenny Forbes with their respective thoughts; of fish, and tips.

Am I cynical? Maybe. Shorn of the myth that often surrounds him, much of it of his own making, you find the real man when you get to know the ghillie.

Getting to know Alec Ross is not easy. Alec does not fit the popular concept of the Scottish ghillie at all. He is small, he has a beaky nose and deep-sunk eyes which peer out at you from beneath the brim of his deerstalker hat. The bottom half of him is usually clad in outsize tweed plus-fours, his legs sticking out bird-like from beneath the turn-ups. He is possessed of a clackety voice which rises to a shrill falsetto when he gets excited. I am not exactly sure of it, but I would put his age somewhere in his middle fifties. His accent at least proclaims his ethnic origin. I have only once seen him wearing a kilt, at a local wedding, and I must say even on that occasion he would have been neglected by any tourist as a typical Highlander to photograph.

Alec must have seen hundreds of salmon hooked, but he never loses his enthusiasm for the occasion. Or his excitement. His mind is with the fish and not the fisherman. The salmon at the end of the line becomes his personal problem, and whoever is holding the rod merely an accessory to its capture.

Short of grabbing hold of the rod himself, Alec's contribution to landing the fish is *de facto* limited to the use of his voice alone: what he would do in the circumstances, what the fisherman must do; a series of staccato instructions delivered at high speed, loud but not always very clear.

I could appreciate the discord which seemed to have arisen between Sir Ernest Cantrell and Alec Ross.

# Chapter Three

# Sir Ernest Cantrell

The following day (it was a Sunday) Sir Ernest Cantrell came down to breakfast just as I was about to leave the table. I sat down again. He said, 'I suppose you must think I'm a right old humbug telling your wife how I caught that salmon yesterday, when you saw what actually happened.'

I said something about it being an unlikely fisherman who didn't shoot a bit of a line, and at least he'd landed the salmon.

'But I didn't, Alec Ross gaffed it.' Sir Ernest spoke with only the faintest trace of a North Country accent when he was choosing his words carefully, as he was now; the accent had been more pronounced yesterday when I heard him describing to my wife how he caught the salmon. 'I've been a politician you know, and politicians aren't noted for their modesty. It comes naturally to make a silk purse out of a sow's ear. I know what I made of that salmon, and it was more of a pig's arse than a sow's ear.' He looked at me and grinned; an engaging grin, the eyes holding mine lacking the contrition of real embarrassment, but making a smiling gesture of it. I think if I had not seen what actually happened, I should have believed every word of his account of the capture of yesterday's salmon.

He continued, 'Catching people is all very well. I learnt the hard way. You try winning the hearts and minds of fifteen hundred delegates at a union conference. You have to tell them a little of what they want to hear, keep quiet about a lot of what they don't want to hear, and convince them what they are hearing is the truth. That's politics, the art of the plausible. Some people might call a good deal of it bluff. I suppose it's the same with catching fish, you've got to bluff 'em until you've landed them. I don't seem to have learnt to do that yet. I couldn't bluff that Alec Ross either, so I tried it on your wife instead. Comes naturally, you see.' Now he was trying to catch me as well, and I did not mind.

But how was it that such an unlikely candidate for our carefully selected guest list came to be staying at Balmeanie?

It came about this way. My cousin Guy Lewis, whose career in the old Colonial Office had landed him as Chief Secretary to the Governor of one of the Windward Islands, introduced us to Sir Ernest Cantrell. Apparently Cantrell had been appointed by the then Labour Government to replace the outgoing Governor whilst Guy Lewis was still the resident Chief Secretary. According to Guy, Sir Ernest had worked his way up the political ladder, starting as a paid official in the National Union of Railwaymen, then standing for Parliament and being elected as Labour member for a Yorkshire constituency. When Labour came to power Ernest Cantrell was rewarded for his loyalty, first as a trade unionist then as an MP, by a knighthood and by his removal from mainstream politics to a governorship abroad, where his forceful personality would not rock the Party boat at home.

Guy told the story of Sir Ernest Cantrell's arrival *en poste*.

The glitterati of the Government House staff had been assembled in the drawing room to meet the new Governor. He addressed them thus: 'While you lot,' he said, buttering his pronunciation with his lapsed native Yorkshire, 'were huntin' and shootin', I were shuntin', and tootin'.' Guy, like his fellow administrators, had been awaiting the new Governor's arrival with some apprehension. Ernest Cantrell knew it, played on it, and won. By the end of his first year in office, his staff would have done anything for him.

Guy Lewis, in particular, despite the dissimilarity in age and background, became a firm friend.

I learnt all this when Guy and his wife were up at Balmeanie, and he had asked me if I would do him a favour and have a friend of his to stay. 'Oh, he'll be happy to pay the

# COCH - Y - BONDDU BOOKS

Paul Morgan

Pentrehedyn Street
Machynlleth, Powys
SY20 8DJ, U.K.

Tel. 01654 702837
Fax. 01654 702857

Modern and Antiquarian Books
for the Angler and Sportsman

going rate,' Guy said, 'but I think it would do him a power of good to come. You see, his wife died last year, and he's been trying to find his feet again ever since. It's not that he hasn't got enough to do. He's got plenty. When his term as Governor was up — that was before his wife died — he got involved in all manner of things; I won't bore you with them all, look him up in *Who's Who* if you're interested. His wife's death left a great big hole in Ernest's life, not just the emotional side of it but the occupational one as well. He'd got few interests in anything other than his work, so far as I could judge. Home was the flip side of the coin, the relaxation side; Betty his wife was all he needed, except, to judge by the occasional chance remark, children. Unfortunately there were none. When home was only an empty house, there was nothing else for him but work. I think, though, I may have found a cure for this unhealthy addiction. It's fishing.'

'But why fishing?' I asked. 'Seems a most unlikely occupation to take up for a man with the sort of background you describe, especially quite late in life.'

'You'd think so wouldn't you. Soon after Betty died, I had Ernest to stay down in Hampshire. I suppose he'd got to know us pretty well after two and a half years in a small island where we were, so to speak, his professional next of kin. We didn't think he'd want to do any socialising when he was with us, and although he said he'd be happy pottering about, we had to think of ways of keeping his mind off things. As you know I've got a bit of fishing down there, so I took Ernest with me one day, and instructed him in the basic art of dry-fly fishing for trout. He was fascinated.'

Now we, too, were hosts to Sir Ernest's new-found passion.

I explained we did not fish on Sundays, and asked Ernest Cantrell what he would like to do after he had finished breakfast. He said if we could provide him with a packed lunch, he would quite like to go for a drive. He had a map. Where would I recommend him to go? I suggested a route and in due course off he went.

Supper on Sundays is a movable feast for us and usually cold, whether we have people staying or not. Ernest Cantrell got back from his drive at teatime, and after supper we went for a walk together by the river. It was one of those magical evenings after a hot day: with the heat gone, the dusk slowly stealing the daylight but itself reluctant to be stolen by the dark, the stark shapes of the pine trees on the far bank of the river reflected in the burnished surface of the pools; total peace all around, broken only by the splash of a salmon throwing his weight about the pool as if in protest at his long confinement there. A woodcock flew over the river towards the trees, a harbinger of the twilight. If I happened to be down here I usually saw one at this time, glancing up automatically, anticipating the bird's arrival and silent purposeful flight overhead. We remained silent, too.

Eventually my companion said, 'I think I'm going to enjoy myself here'. When we got back to the Lodge, and were having a last glass of whisky before bed, Ernest Cantrell said, 'I suppose Guy Lewis has told you a bit about me.'

'A bit,' I said.

'Well, I'll tell you something about Guy Lewis. He's one of the best friends I ever had. He's younger than me, we come from completely different backgrounds, but I soon found out he was always there when I needed him, first as an adviser, then as a friend. He knew Sir Ernest Cantrell, but he also got to know Ernie Cantrell as well, and he knew how both of them were knocked flat when Betty died. I'd hate to make you feel embarrassed by pouring my heart out right at the start of my visit, but you are Guy's cousin, and the two of you are responsible for me being here. You must be wondering why a chap with my background comes to stay in a Highland lodge to fish for salmon. If you'll bear with me, I'd just like to explain why I've come; especially after having got off to rather a bad start.'

'Please don't think it was a bad start,' I said. 'Alec Ross is not exactly what the Italians would term *simpatico*. Inspiring optimism in the guests he takes fishing is not his strong point.

You could be forgiven for taking a dose of it yourself afterwards. I have. But do go on.'

'When Betty died, work was the only place I could lose myself, in the complications of one situation or another. As soon as I stopped working I started thinking, and I thought about her. I still do, for that matter, but I don't feel so sorry for myself now. We had a good life together, Betty and I, and I'm grateful for the memory of that. Now I've got to do something about a different sort of life. Home and work, both of them have turned out well for me — with a few limitations. But I never tried — allowed myself — to discover a third dimension as an insurance policy against anything going wrong with either. Home isn't the same place now and I've learnt to live with that. Work, I think I've done my fair share, and anyway I'm fed up with trying to keep the heel-snappers at bay. Thanks to Guy I think I could be on my way to finding that third dimension that I've never discovered, in fishing. Marvellous how life compensates, isn't it? You lose something and you find something.'

'Depends how hard you look,' I said. 'But what do you hope to find in fishing? If you'll forgive me saying so, you've made a late start.'

'All the more to catch up on then,' replied Ernest Cantrell. 'I've kept you up late enough already. I'll tell you at the end of next week what I've found here. But I can tell you now that it won't be all I'm looking for — at least I hope not; if you find exactly what you are looking for right at the start there isn't much point in going on looking. Now I must let you go to bed. I've got a busy day tomorrow as well — gaining some degree of credibility with Alec Ross.'

When I went out for my pre-breakfast stroll on Monday the sun was already beginning its climb into a cloudless sky. The little rain which there had been last week had run off quickly, as it does in the Struie, which has only the burns to feed it, and no loch to act as a cistern storing up the headwaters for a while. I didn't think much of Sir Ernest Cantrell's chances of widening his fishing experience today, except to discover

21

that supine salmon sheltering from the sun are totally uninterested in the fly – any fly.

Alec Ross, when I went to see him, thought it was a waste of time to fish at all, as it probably was, but I persuaded him to consider the psychological aspect of things: seeing fish was believing that you might be able to catch them. 'Aye,' he replied, 'and mebbe so you could, if you were to try them wi' a worrm.'

'Don't you go teaching Sir Ernest the secrets of low-water worming for salmon,' I said. 'Maybe he'll resort to it one day, but not while he's here.'

I arranged that Alec would take Ernest Cantrell out in the morning, at least until the sun was right on the water and there wasn't a chance. They could try again in the evening. After breakfast the two of them set off. I watched them go, Alec a few paces behind Sir Ernest, carrying the rod. I guessed by the downward tilt of his head that he was not in the mood for conversation. I walked back towards the house thinking how I could best use the day. We had no one else staying, and I went to have a word with Jim Fraser about the sheep.

It was just before twelve that I went in search of my guest. I walked upstream towards the Falls O' Meanie. Working on the assumption that where the greatest number of fish are congregated the odds are more in favour of one of them behaving like an idiot and snatching the fly, I thought it most likely that Alec would head that way. It did also occur to me that with a seat and some shade from the trees beside the pool, it was as comfortable a place as any to pass the time of day when not actually fishing. No sign of them, however. I retraced my steps. Then I heard voices coming from the direction of the bridge carrying the drive over the river. I proceeded in that direction.

I heard the unmistakable staccato of Alec's voice. As I got closer I was able to hear what he was saying – *con brio*: 'Aye, they were the ones, the Four MTs, two-six-oh, you stoked up the firebox – many's the time I done it mesel' – and we'd go thunderin' down the track along the straight. You could get her up to near seventy on the downhill gradient frae Aultbuie. Real sense of power it gave shovelling on the coal, knowing it was you keepin' her going at that speed.'

There were the two of them sitting in the shade beneath the span of the bridge. Ernest Cantrell saw me first. He said, as if inviting me to join in their conversation, 'Alec here reckoned there was no chance of a salmon so we chucked fishing. We're having a bit of a chat about the old days of steam on the railways. You didn't tell me he'd been a railwayman.'

The days of Ernest Cantrell's visit succeeded one another, sunny and rainless: ideal for lazing around, picnics by the lochside, visits to the golden sands within forty minutes' drive at Portwhinnie; perfect holiday weather. For all but fishermen. Even Ernest, as I now came to know him, realised the impossibility of catching salmon under such conditions, and I feared he might lose interest. Fortunately I had reckoned without the character which was being revealed to me, the chief part of which, I soon discovered, was a resolution to throw himself wholeheartedly into whatever he undertook. He asked me interminable questions about the habits of salmon. He wooed Alec Ross for his experiences as he would a constituent for his vote. He spent hours up at the Falls O' Meanie, watching through polaroid glasses the fish imprisoned there. He read books on fishing out of the big Victorian bookcase in the hall, as I imagine at one time he had read books on political theory.

Neither Alec nor I could help responding to this consuming interest in the habits of fish, and we did our best to provide alternatives to fishing for salmon with the fly in the conventional manner. Ernest Cantrell asked me one evening why Alec had suggested that a larger than usual pattern mounted on a double hook, fished slowly and deep, might produce results in the Falls O' Meanie pool, when I had told him that in low water you ought to fish a very small fly near the surface. The water was low, so why this difference of opinion? Ernest asked.

The following day, as a penance, I told Alec to take Sir Ernest to the Cairnloch. I had already asked the latter if he minded a bumpy ride in a Land-Rover, followed by a very stiff uphill climb, in exchange for a glimpse of earthly paradise and the chance to catch trout the like of which he would not have seen before.

The Cairnloch lies 1,800 feet above sea level in total seclusion from any human dwelling. It contains golden-bellied trout decorated on the sides with roundels of vivid red, the most beautiful brown trout that I have ever seen, and they can be quite big for a Highland loch, up to two pounds or more in weight. The only drawback is getting to the Cairnloch. A five-mile jolting in a Land-Rover over a boulder-strewn track, then from where the track ends in a broken-down bridge a further two miles on foot following the headwaters of the Struie; after that the real work begins, a climb of a further mile and a half up the steep side of the glen. A cascading burn is the first indication the weary climber gets that he has reached journey's end — outwardbound. A final clamber up the rocky face of the burn's outfall, and there at last is the Cairnloch, stretching out before you like a vision of the promised land.

When Ernest Cantrell got back that evening he said, 'That damned ghillie of yours has half-killed a superannuated Labour politician with a distinguished record fighting for workers' rights, taking me where he did today. When I reached the end of that climb I thought I'd passed over the Great Divide and was getting my first glimpse of Heaven. Here, look at these.' He showed me four golden trout.

'Worth the climb, were they?' I asked.

A host worthy of the name feels directly responsible for keeping his guests amused, whether they are paying or not. With plenty of fishing but without enough water this can be a problem. It can be more of a problem with some guests than others. I was reminded of this recently when I had reason to call in at a hotel for the well-heeled anglers who come to fish another of the Kyle rivers. There was no water, and little or no chance of a salmon. As I entered the hotel lounge, which should at this time of the morning have been more or less empty, I encountered a restless wall of open newspapers, some of which were lowered at my arrival to reveal the readers' basilisk stares at this intruder on their misery of paying good money for no fishing. Now I happen to know that there are any number of hill lochs which could have occupied the newspaper readers' time, and come the evening there are sea trout to be caught as well. But that would not have answered the 'How Did You Get Ons?' down south. It had to be the number of salmon caught.

We listened to the weather forecast each evening, anxious for the words of comfort, 'The north-east of Scotland will have heavy rain followed by showers and bright intervals.' We heard them not. As we met at breakfast, I would anxiously ask, 'Any idea what you would like to do with yourself today? I'm afraid the river looks pretty useless.' This particular morning Ernest said, 'Didn't you tell me that sea trout which were uncatchable by day would take at night, even when the water was low? Are there any sea trout in the Struie?'

'No, but there are in the Balmeanie Burn, and a few salmon too. There are only a few pools worth fishing, and they are quite a distance apart, difficult fishing too, with the trees. It's useless by day, except after a spate.'

'But at night?'

'You could try. Not many bother. Look here, if you can amuse yourself today — you might care to go and explore up the burn, take your polaroids with you — then after dinner we can go up there and see if there's anything doing.'

From the strictly practical point of view — catching sea trout — the evening was not particularly successful. I caught one three-quarter-pound fish, Ernest Cantrell lost two casts and had, so he told me excitedly, one tug. I did not realise it at the time, but for him it was the beginning of a love affair with that burn. I discerned the first sign of this the following morning, when Ernest said he would give the river a miss, and have a walk up the burn with a view to fishing there again that evening. 'No need for you to bother to come,' he said, 'I'll be quite happy up there on my own.'

There were only a couple of days left before Ernest Cantrell was due to leave. More for form's sake than anything else, I consulted Alec Ross about the possibilities of a final salmon. 'No a chance,' he said, 'unless we was to try with the worrm, or else in the Falls Pool wi'...'

I knew what was coming and interrupted. 'Alec,' I said, 'I don't think Sir Ernest really wants to catch a salmon that badly. It's my guess he'd much rather fish where and how he wants to than where and how he's told to, whether or not he catches a fish.'

'Fine, but he needs to learn tae fish properly, and he needs to ken the river.'

'He is learning, all the time; from you, from me, but most of all he's learning from himself what he wants to make of fishing. And I think this place will teach him that better than you or I ever could.'

At the end of the week Ernest Cantrell departed without having caught another salmon. He did catch two sea trout in the Balmeanie Burn, and told me that he'd been broken by another much larger fish. He gave me a graphic description of what happened. Ernest knew he was on safe ground this time because there were no witnesses. But I believed him all the same. The following morning Ann and I waved and stood watching as the maroon Volvo estate car, which I had first seen a fortnight ago, drove off down the drive and over the bridge to become lost in the trees the other side of the river.

Five days later I had a letter from Ernest, and I quote from it:

'When I first came to stay with you, you asked me as a late starter what I hoped to find in fishing. I said that whatever it was, it had to be something that I would want to go on looking for: I did not expect to find it like a lost key, at Balmeanie or anywhere else. Now I am not a very religious man, you would hardly expect it of a materialistic socialist politician, but I am beginning to understand why fishermen feature so largely in the New Testament. Theirs is a peace which passes understanding, until you begin to understand it yourself. I found that. I found too what a marvellous companion nature can be. I have not really been introduced to her before. Now that I have met her in a place of her own, I am sure she will forgive me for taking a few (a very few) of her fish for the pleasure of her company. As I drove away last Saturday, I stopped the car the other side of the river, and got out for a last look at this place from where I had set out on my expedition fourteen days ago knowing so little and learning so much. Alec Ross's farewell words came back to me, 'Gang warily, Sir Ernest, forbye we want to see you back again next year.'

I came across that letter many years later. The other letters of thanks in the file I was looking through were mostly the sort you scrunch up and throw in the waste-paper basket when you have read them through once. I wondered why I had not done so. I recognised the writer only by the address at the top of the writing paper, or the signature at the end of the letter. Yet Ann and I had seen these people come and seen them go: welcomed them, arranged for their comfort and sport whilst they were with us, listened to their delights when there were fish to be caught, their despair when there were none; heard their stories and a good deal of their life history, noticed their moods and judged them according to our own lights. A fishing holiday reveals many facets of character — disclosed and undisclosed.

So what did I recall of these people who have been our guests, what did they take with them from this remote corner of the Highlands — other than stories of fish caught and lost? Unlike Ernest Cantrell, they do not say. What did they leave behind? That is not for them to say: it is for Ann and I, for Alec Ross and Jim Fraser, for Mrs McKenzie and Flora.

I thought it would be a pleasant winter's occupation, when

the darkness falls at four o'clock, to tell what I remember of some of them.

The title? Oh yes, Jock Robertson was responsible for that — indirectly.

'When the Bunburys [who had sold the place to my aunt] were here,' Jock Robertson told me one day soon after we had arrived, 'Elsie Bunbury had a habit of getting up from chair or table at unlikely moments, saying "I must go to the rod room, my dear." At first people thought it must be an expression she'd developed for saying she wanted to go to the loo. Then one day a visitor to Balmeanie, who happened to be a local, found his path blocked by a car with its front wheel in the ditch. He got out to investigate and saw that there was a recumbent body slumped in the front seat. He recognised it as Elsie's, not difficult because she was a very large lady. He called out anxiously, "Are you all right, Elsie?" By this time he was close to the car window, which was open; there was a distinct smell of gin in the air. "It's all right, my dear, just looking for my handbag," came the reply.

'After that,' said Jock, 'people began to guess what "Going to the rod room" meant.'

We do not have a rod room, not as such. Fishing rods, when they are assembled, are put away in a long wooden chest on the veranda. I suppose the smallish room at the back of the house where fishing tackle, rifles, and the like are kept could be called the rod room. It is a room some fourteen feet square, panelled in dark pitch-pine, with a great many racks and cupboards.

When we opened one of the cupboards, a large one, we found it crammed with empty gin bottles.

Part of Balmeanie's rich history? Not really. But what would you have me call this collection of stories associated with a place built by a maker of sauce, sold by a laird from London, bought by a maiden lady from Bournemouth, and inherited by a Berkshire estate agent: *Memoirs Of A Highland Shooting Lodge*? So *Tales From the Rod Room* it is.

# Chapter Four

# The Brothers Pool

I should like to describe for you as best I can the fishing on the Balmeanie Burn. The Struie river is the main thoroughfare for the salmon, the burn attracting only its native children who grew to smolthood there. On return, they follow the course of the river for some ten miles before the current of the burn enters and seduces them with the sweet smell of home. The select band of burn-spawned salmon leave the main river, and chance their luck with the spates to run this unpredictable stream, to where, two miles upstream on one arm of it, their journey ends in a rocky cauldron; the other arm leaves them no hiding place in the small heather-clad pools of the open hillside. These few salmon are joined by the more prolific sea trout, who also prefer the byways of the river system to the highway.

The fisherman's way up the Balmeanie Burn, unless he or she proposes to walk the whole twisting course, is by means of a track which runs alongside the burn; or it does where the water's course is over even ground, for the track deserts the burn in wide loops where the stream takes its own more direct course across country. The track was constructed during the palmy days of the original proprietor, when money was little object. It leads through to another part of the original estate. During the 1960s it was made impassable, to stop poachers bringing out their cargo of slaughtered deer by night. Now the track, still in good condition, leads only to a shepherd's bothy and a ruined lodge.

Improvements, man-made, are confined to the Struie itself.

Platforms and walkways have been constructed here to ease the fisherman's task of putting a fly over the fish; casting has been made easier by the erection of wooden staging pinned to the steep rock wall along some of the pools. On the burn only one attempt has been made to improve on nature for the benefit of fishermen.

The idea was to dam back the stream to form an artificial loch in which the salmon and sea trout would congregate. At least, that was my predecessor Kenneth Bunbury's idea. At considerable expense he had constructed a concrete dam, complete with fish-pass, a foot wide on top, ten times that width at the base. The burn in summer spate — brown raging water banked high over the impediment of the dam — gave no more than an angry warning of the elemental force that would be unleashed against it during the winter. All that remains now are jagged blocks of concrete tossed around by the current their original structure sought to restrain, weathered, yet lacking the shape and texture of the natural rock; the only memorial to what has come to be known as Bunbury's Folly.

Walk up the Balmeanie Burn in high summer when the water is low, and it looks the most unpromising route for any migratory fish to take; long stretches of boulder-strewn watercourse and rocky canyon separate what few pools there are along its course. In places there is hardly enough water to cover a salmon's back. But a cloudburst in the hills, or a more continuous period of rain, changes the picture altogether. First there is a raging turmoil of water, the sheer force of it frightening to watch — nothing caught in the headlong rush of that current could stand a chance, you think, watching the flotsam careering downstream. Except somehow the fish, you know, are there, having seen them last week in serried ranks against the rock wall of a pool. This pool is now no longer recognisable as such, nor any other. The Balmeanie Burn is one long snaking seething torrent of water.

When the rain stops it takes only a matter of hours for the burn to start falling. Now is the time to go fishing there. The water looks like black coffee, dark but getting ever more translucent. Where a few hours earlier the water boiled, it now bulges and glides over the boulders. Places where you would not bother to fish look as if they might hold fish. The necks of the pools, where pools there are in low water, are still all bubbles and white water, but the tails begin to look increasingly inviting, especially when you see in one of them a newly arrived salmon show. This is the only time the Balmeanie Burn is really worth fishing during the daylight hours. And it is pure delight. For two main reasons: first because there is no established lore as to where, why, and how you should fish, and second because of the unexpected. That bulge you noticed in the place you would not normally bother to fish, because the water is only a foot deep, brings the golden flash of a turning salmon in response to your cast. And having hooked it, what a struggle it is to land. At the end of it you go home with maybe one or two salmon, saying to yourself, 'all my own work'.

The following day the burn has run off. You might strike lucky, but the magic few hours have passed and the water is falling still, and with it your chances of catching a salmon or a seatrout, by daylight. But what of the new arrivals that came with yesterday's spate?

I am always intrigued by estate agents' advertisements for fishing. X number of named pools, they state, as if the naming of a pool is some guarantee of the quantity of fish that it contains. There is only one named pool on the Balmeanie Burn, that is, if you do not count Bunbury's Folly, which is a pool no longer. The other pots, linns and scours which form the rungs on this stony ladder have no name, but many hold a stock of fish to be seen, if not to be caught with the fly, during sociable hours.

The fish, mostly sea trout with a few salmon, cannot be seen in the deep pots, and in my experience are virtually uncatchable, except perhaps with a worm dropped in and carried down to the depths by the current. I am not snooty

31

about this form of fishing, especially in a place like this on the burn where it is most unlikely you will catch anything by other means, but I do not happen to care for it myself; to me the real thrill is that heart-stopping bulge in the water as a fish comes to your fly, and even if there is no ensuing tug, the picture remains in your mind of what might have been, and may be tomorrow. No, not for me the unseen worm.

The other holding places on the burn display their wares better: a long, deepish channel has a salmon or two lying motionless half-way down where the current eases. Or at a widening of the burn on a bend; a likely spot you think, and lie down to peer over the bank into the calmer water, there directly beneath are the shapes of the dozen or so sea trout écheloned hard up against the steep rock. Sometimes a scared fish shoots upstream, disturbed by your silhouette across the window of his resting place. No named pools, just those which you discover for yourself.

If you drove the three miles up to where the track finally parts company with the stream, climbing up through the trees to emerge in wide open stretches of heather and peat-hag, you would have passed unnoticed the one named pool there is on the Balmeanie Burn. Had you stopped your car a mile or so back, got out and scrambled down through the silver birch and bracken, rushes and bog, for a hundred yards or so until you reached the bank of the stream, low on your side, high on the other where the boulders and rough grass meet the heather of the hill beyond, you would have found the Brothers Pool.

Here the current chases down a narrow channel in the rock for ten yards or so, then according to its strength either sweeps round the steep containing bank before subsiding, or, swollen by rain, takes a more direct course, swirling along the bank on which you stand. When the burn is running low there is always a deep still basin of dark water in the middle of the pool; it ripples away over a shallow boulder-strewn tail. When the burn is running high this basin is all current, and the tail a glide of sliding water smooth and undulating over the boulders in the tail. The Brothers is the classic pattern of salmon pool on a very small scale.

In normal conditions, which usually means the burn is a bit low, the fish either lie where you can see them, deep down against the wall where the current emerges from its narrow conduit; or where you cannot see them, in the basin in the centre of the pool. Neither party will take any notice of your fly.

Come up here, however, as the day goes out of the sky, leaving the west aglow with a bar of light, and the colour drains from the landscape so that its features are recognisable by shape alone. Then the pool mirrors the sky in the west, its surface metallic and impenetrable, and as you look down towards the tail, there is a sudden movement, a wake which ends in a swirl. Then a fish jumps clear of the water, its body arched and seen against the sky, an unforgettable imprint on the memory. More wakes, more swirls, as the salmon play in the shallows before returning to their lies for the night. Then it is the turn of the sea trout to divert themselves after having lain supine all day; their dance at dusk is less impressive than that of the salmon, but to the fisherman often more rewarding. By this time it is as dark as it ever gets on a summer's night six hundred and fifty miles north of London.

Some people regard fishing for sea trout at night as keeping unsociable hours, but with the exception of the brown trout in the lochs, it is the only form of fishing there is in low water. As Ernest Cantrell found out. And even if you do not stay late, that hour or so at dusk is worth a whole morning spent flogging a dead river in the sunlight.

And so guests who do not mind the unsociable hours, and are either adventurous enough to go exploring, or fed up with fishing for stale salmon, sometimes make their way up the Balmeanie Burn towards nightfall. Roger Ballantyne was one such person.

Roger is an ex-Army officer turned stockbroker, and he comes here each year. He has fished for various kinds of fish all over the world. He and his wife Jane were staying with us

33

one year in August, and had struck one of those periods, all too frequent in the late summer, when we had been without rain for days on end. The river was full of salmon but not so full of water, and Roger was having a thin time of it. On the Wednesday evening of his last week, he decided to go up the Balmeanie Burn after the sea trout, saying he would not be back until late and not to wait up for him. At about half-past eleven I was reading the newspaper before going up to bed when I heard the front door open; Ann and Roger's wife had already gone upstairs. It was hardly likely to be anyone else but Roger, and I went into the hall to meet him.

'Back early,' I said, 'nothing doing then?'

'Oh yes,' he said, 'I got a couple of nice fish before I got scared off.'

'What on earth do you mean?'

'Give me a drink and I'll tell you, I really feel rather ashamed of myself.'

We went into the little room we rather grandly call the smoking room. I gave Roger a drink and we sat down. This is more or less what Roger Ballantyne told me.

'I went straight up to that pool you call the Brothers Pool. I don't know why I haven't been up there before, because it is a perfect-looking place for a sea trout in that tail. I didn't start fishing immediately, I thought I would wait until the light was gone from the sky. It's a smallish pool and I didn't want to scare the fish by starting too soon. The midges nearly ate me alive; I never know which is worse, them or the stink of that ointment stuff you put on your face and hands.'

'I try smoking my pipe,' I said, 'But it doesn't work.'

'Anyway, when the fish activity began in the tail of the pool, the bow-waves and the turns, and the racing back up the pool again, I couldn't resist it any longer, and I began fishing. Chasing around like that, you'd think, wouldn't you, that the salmon would include your fly in their game of tag, but it doesn't often happen that way. Still, the temptation to fish in amongst all this activity is overwhelming. It was getting quite dark when I caught the first sea trout, right up in the neck of the pool as it happens. I netted it, and took a break. A bad mistake that, if I'd gone on fishing my attention might have stayed with the fish, but I doubt it. Then the utter stillness of the place got hold of me. And the loneliness. Why was it called the Brothers Pool? Had one of the brothers — whoever they were — drowned there? Something had to have happened for the pool to be called by such an unusual name. What?'

I had been told why the pool was called the Brothers, but I thought I would keep the story to myself for the time being.

'I pulled myself together and went on fishing,' continued Roger. 'I would have been grateful for any of the usual noises you get in the countryside down south after dark: owls, a fox barking, anything to remind me that I wasn't alone, and that night birds and animals were about their business around me. But here, utter silence, except for the sucking noise of the water at my feet. The Brothers who? What had they done here in this remote spot? Once or twice I glanced over my shoulder with a feeling that someone was watching me: nonsense of course, who could be up here, and why? I hooked the other sea trout, landed it, and wondered whether I should go or stay. At that moment there was a clatter of stones on the far bank. I nearly jumped out of my skin. I shone my torch in the direction of the noise, and for a moment the beam caught the reflection of a pair of eyes in the deep shadow of the steep bank, then they were gone. There was another clattering of the stones, then everything was quiet again except for the sound of running water. The silence was all the deeper for the recent intrusion of noise: I could stand its intensity no longer, and I left.

'As I climbed up the slope to the track where I had parked the car, I stopped for a moment after some fifty yards and looked back. The pool was hidden from view, but the steep bank on the far side reared up a dark solid mass against the sky, and silhouetted on top of it were the horned heads of half a dozen stags. To relieve my feelings I shouted at them. My voice carried into the distance, bringing not the trace of an echo. With relief I reached the car and switched on the lights.

'And here I am a grown man, an ex-soldier, and frightened of the dark.'

'Well at least you caught a couple of sea trout,' I said. I did not prolong the conversation. I had been out on the hill all day with Jim Fraser, looking at the sheep, and I was tired and wanted to go to bed.

As I made my way to our room I heard the rain beating against the window in the passage. When I got up the following morning it had obviously been raining hard all night, there were puddles in the potholes in the drive. It was still raining. At least Roger Ballantyne won't have to go up to the Balmeanie Burn tonight, I thought, and considered the possibility of going there myself this afternoon if the rain let up a little.

I had hardly finished my breakfast (I admit to trying to get there first so that I can eat it alone) when Flora McKenzie came to say that Alec Ross was waiting in the kitchen to see me. When Alec Ross waits to see me during the fishing season, instead of my going in search of him, it usually means that the river looks promising. An hour later the Ballantynes and he set off, not to reappear until teatime, bringing with them three salmon and an aura of contentment. Bath, drink, dinner, and coffee in the drawing room, before Roger Ballantyne brought up the subject of his experience last night.

'I have only once before been frightened out fishing,' he said, 'and that was the rank, sweaty kind of fear you feel when you face some sudden danger like being chased by a bull − in my case it was a shark − I'll tell you about that in a minute, if you're interested. I think there is quite a difference between being frightened and being afraid; one is fear of what you can see, the other is fear of what you cannot see, one confronts you, the other creeps up on you. Now last night I had an overwhelming sense of trespassing where I ought not to be; someone might at any moment lay a hand on my shoulder and say, "What are you doing here, don't you know this place is private?" There was no feeling of evil influence, only of pressure on me to leave. And so leave I did.'

'Well I must say, I've been up to that pool hundreds of times at night,' I said, 'and I've never felt spooked. Now then, what was the other occasion you were talking about when you were scared out fishing?' Looking back on it, perhaps I spoke a little impatiently, thinking Roger's experience no more than a figment of his imagination.

'No,' he replied his thoughts not yet ready to be shifted, 'I've got a question to ask you first, then I'll tell you. Do you happen to know how that pool came to get its name?'

'Well, as a matter of fact I do. About fifteen miles away from here there's another lodge called Strathcannock. It belonged to a Mr and Mrs Flemington. They had three children, the eldest a girl, and two boys only a couple of years apart in age, all of them away at school. Apart from a trout loch there was no fishing at Strathcannock, and during the school holidays the boys used to come over here. They were told they could go where they wanted on the Balmeanie Burn. Well of course they did, and got to know the place like the backs of their hands. They caught little brown trout, and the occasional sea-trout, but never a salmon. Then one day, after a spate in that pool where you were last night − it had no name then − both of them caught a salmon, their first. It was a natural, the pool had to be called the Brothers. It was. Now you tell me about your shark.'

'I'm not at all ashamed of being frightened on that occasion, anyone would have been. It happened at the Jordanian port of Aqaba, very much in the news these days. I hardly recognise the place now the way it has been built up, only when the TV camera catches the shoreline from the sea does the vivid contrast of colours come back to me: the sea an extraordinary cobalt blue, and the land what I believe the artists call burnt sienna. When I was there at the end of the forties there was nothing more than a jetty, a few buildings. A couple of miles down the gulf stood a large featureless building, the fish factory owned by an enterprising Arab by the name of Asad. I don't know why I should remember his name, but I do.

'The borders of three Arab countries, Egypt, Transjordan (as it then was), and Saudi Arabia met within ten miles of Aqaba, and thrusting down between two of them came the Israelis, newly-independent of the British mandate and eager for new territory and a Red Sea port – Eilat. We, one battalion of the British Army, were there to see they went no further into Arab territory. That is all I need to say about the political situation. The military situation, as is often the case when the Army is required to act the policeman, was one of limited activity and plenty of boredom. Bathing and exploring were the two main leisure activities.

'I had managed to get a sailing dinghy transported from our base in the Canal Zone. Of this boat I remember only that it was about twelve feet long, and had a freeboard of a foot or so when on an even keel. To me the principal purpose of having a boat is to use it for mucking around in or for fishing. I am not deeply into the intricacies of sailing. On this occasion I persuaded a friend to join me, and we set out on the blue waters of the gulf armed with the best the NAAFI could provide in fishing equipment, the sort of stuff you buy from a fancy goods shop on the south coast of England.

'Not surprisingly, it was difficult to obtain the sort of useful information you can usually pick up from the locals about the best bait to use and the best place to go; first of all there was the language difficulty, and secondly the local Arabs preferred to use explosives as the most effective method of obtaining fish. For bait we therefore took with us a can of assorted fish heads and other offal obtained from Mr Asad's factory. Where to go? Confronted with an expanse of featureless blue water, and little information about what it contained apart from sharks, it was more a question of where not to go. And the answer was clear – not too far from the shore.

'I have often wondered why it is called the Red Sea. There are, apparently, three possible explanations: one that it was in fact called 'the sea of reeds'; another that it derives from the coral bed; and the third from the reflection of the eastern sky in its waters. On the evidence of my own eyes, there are no reeds, the coral does not show up red, and the reflection of the sky is blue, a deep blue like the feathers on a peacock's breast. But once afloat, except in very deep water, you can see right down to the bottom, a fact which was to have a distinct bearing on the outcome of our fishing expedition.

'We got off to a bad start. Rounding the harbour jetty, we were forced out into the open gulf before turning landwards and making for a position close off-shore where we intended to start fishing. Looking down the gulf we watched spellbound as, a couple of hundred yards away, some long narrow fish ricocheted in bursts of spray over the wavelets after an unseen quarry. Must be barracuda, we thought. It would be unfortunate if we were to hinder them in their pursuit. I had heard about barracuda, but never seen them before. These fish, two or three foot long, torpedo shaped, and armed with a mouthful of pointed teeth, tear into their prey like bullets. Someone had told me they were more dangerous than sharks. We edged closer to the shore.

'I remember only the main events of what happened next that afternoon, and I remember them most vividly.

'There was not much happening with the fishing. I rather think we had some difficulty in attaching the bait to our hooks; each time we tried to do so, the rapidly decomposing flesh crumbled away and we threw much of it overboard. Perhaps in the light of subsequent events doing so was a mistake.

'I was gazing vacantly into the depths beneath the boat, and I could make out the shape of the coral fifteen feet or so beneath me. Now this I remember quite clearly, the conformation of the seabed changed and seemed to solidify; it was as if we had drifted over a different texture of bottom, less variegated and closer to the surface. It was at this moment that I heard my companion, Tony, praying fervently, "Hail Mary full of grace". Those words only I remember. Then the realisation of what I was seeing came full upon me. The bottom was obscured by an enormous fish.

'You know how it is when a car you are in goes out of control. There is absolutely nothing you can do except wait for the crash. You are powerless to influence the course of events. It was so on this occasion. We sat bolt upright, a foot above the sea, isolated from it by quarter of an inch of marine-ply. I cannot remember if we looked at one another, I cannot remember if Tony continued to pray aloud; we were each lost to all else except what would happen next. And we sat paralysed waiting for it to happen. In fact, as if to confirm that the apparition we had seen underwater was real, a huge tail broke the surface hard by the stern of the boat. We waited. Then came the glimmering of hope that this was the end of the experience, and the fish, whatever it was, had cleared off. We got the boat moving, and hugged the shore-line and jetty wall back to the safety of the harbour.'

Roger had related this experience as if he was reliving it. Earlier he had spoken with more hesitation. I said, 'Well, I know which experience would have frightened me most. You're hardly likely to face death up at the Brothers Pool.'

'I know, I only mentioned the story of my encounter with that shark — if it was a shark — to make the distinction, as I see it, between being frightened and being afraid. There was nothing whatever to frighten me last night, but by God I was afraid. Why? I wish I knew. Let's just say I would not be such a damn fool again as to go out in a twelve-foot plywood dinghy when there are sharks about, but when in my late forties I am afraid of something I cannot see beside a burn in the Scottish Highlands, I either question my sanity or think there is something damned strange about the place. Let's leave it at that.'

And leave it at that we did. The Ballantynes left on Saturday, two good fishing days later. We were sorry to see them go. And with their going I thought no more of the incident up at the Brothers Pool, until Tuesday of the following week.

I was in Ardroy, picking up the London newspaper which arrives off the midday train from Inverness, and gets collected as and when someone from Balmeanie happens to be in the village. I ran into Jock Robertson doing the same thing. We chatted about this and that, and Jock said, 'You didn't know the Flemingtons over at Strathcannock, did you, they were before your time? You would have liked them, charming and full of fun. They were a great loss when they moved south. The Brothers Pool on the Balmeanie Burn was named after the two boys.' I knew that, I said. 'Those two, Robert and Peter, used to live up that burn during the summer holidays,' continued Jock, 'they had it all to themselves in those days, no one else bothered to go there. Anyhow Peter, the younger of the two, died last week, it was in yesterday's *Telegraph*.'

When I got home I looked through the announcements column of Monday's paper. There under 'Deaths' was the name Flemington. 'On Wednesday the 27th of August, peacefully at home, after an illness borne with great courage and dignity, Peter, aged 56 years, of...' it began.

I wondered if Roger Ballantyne would see the announcement, and if he would make anything of it. No reason why he should really. I have been up to the Brothers Pool by night since on many occasions, and found the place utterly peaceful.

# Chapter Five

# *Anguilla Anguilla*

'An endless moving column of nasty writhing eels, I suppose they were, each three inches or so long, thousands of them, braided together in a slimy rope where the water trickles over the ledge of rock in that little side-stream by the Fank Pool. Ugh, revolting!'

Jane Ballantyne said this one evening at dinner after an excursion by herself to the riverside that afternoon.

'Elvers, baby eels,' interjected her husband knowledgeably. 'They eat them in parts of Gloucestershire. There's an annual elver eating competition at a place called Frampton-on-Severn. I was told the record is a pound in a minute. Won by the village garage mechanic. Or if you want you can have elver cakes.'

'The very thought of eating those horrible creatures makes me feel sick,' said Jane. 'I don't think I'll ever touch smoked eel again.'

'It's all in the mind, you know,' I said. 'Ever since I was a boy I've loved fishing, but eels have always revolted me. It's no good telling me they are absolutely delicious to eat, once I knew it was an eel on my plate — however well disguised — I wouldn't touch a mouthful.'

'I don't know about elvers, but I'll bet if you didn't know it was eel that you were eating, you'd be surprised how delicious the flavour is,' said Roger Ballantyne. 'It's delicate, on the rich side, and the flesh falls neatly off the bone, a real feast. Or you can have the eel cut into fillets you wouldn't recognise.'

'I'm sure you are right, but in my case it's a question of mind over matter. There used to be an old-fashioned fishmonger half way down Drury Lane. They had a metal tank no more than eighteen inches square on the slab, and in it eels, dozens of them, all writhing round one another. I used to stand and watch fascinated. I wouldn't have put my hand in that tank for anything.'

'I'm glad someone is on my side,' said Jane Ballantyne.

'Maybe a dislike of eels runs in the family,' I continued. 'My brother-in-law used to set night lines for them. The night line for catching eels is a pretty crude affair, but effective; thirty yards or so of tough cord tied to a stone, with droppers every foot or so, each one ending in a long-shanked hook. In the evening the hooks were baited with a dead minnow, the stone end of the line chucked out into the river, and the landward end tied firmly to some convenient object on the bank. The following morning my brother-in-law came to collect.

'One morning my mother, who happened to be staying, decided she would like to come and see the collecting process. She arrived as my brother-in-law was hauling in. I was there too, watching. Disentangling a writhing eel from the line, extracting the swallowed hook, and rendering the creature moribund was not a job with which I was prepared to help. My mother was still some way off when my brother-in-law spotted her. He seized one of the eels and gave chase. My mother was a large lady, and until that moment I didn't know she could run – fast – but she let out a shriek and from a standing start she covered the two furlongs back to the road at a speed of which I would never have thought her capable.'

This conversation, or the gist of it, was the prelude to a contribution from the fifth person sitting round the dinner table at Balmeanie that evening. His name was Josh Brandon, and he was a photographer specialising in natural history. So far he had not contributed to the exchange on the subject of elvers and eels. He said now, 'Out there in that river of yours, Charles, there are salmon who have travelled, say, twelve

43

hundred miles from the Greenland coast to get here to reproduce. Those elvers you saw this afternoon, Jane, will travel nearly three times that far when they are fully grown in about ten years time, to get to the Sargasso Sea, also to reproduce. The beautiful silver salmon and the nasty slimy eel, there is so much written and talked about the one, so little about the other. Yet only the European eel, *Anguilla anguilla*, makes that journey, and makes it in six months, travelling from rivers and ponds, overland if necessary where there is moisture, snared in eel-weirs and traps, caught on hooks, hunted by otters and herons, and eventually taking to the ocean fathoms deep, swimming against the Gulf Stream which carried it here as an elver. Quite a life cycle for what most of us regard as an unattractive fish.'

'Adventurous eels may be,' said I, 'but I still find them revolting. Josh, you sound as if you have taken more than a passing interest in their lifestyle, I shouldn't have thought such an unattractive creature offered much scope to the photographer.'

'Maybe not,' said he, 'but I'm interested in survival, and the eel is a born survivor. Then I got involved in a television documentary. When I began talking to people, marine biologists and professional fishermen amongst others, who thought of eels in a different light from most of us, who either hate them or only want to see them on the menu in a fish restaurant, I too began to look on the eel for what it really is, one of nature's original intercontinental travellers. And believe me,' he added as an afterthought, 'that documentary had its moments of high drama when things didn't go according to plan.

'During the making of the film, a professor of zoology was demonstrating the anatomy of the eel. As well as skeletons and dead eels preserved in bottles, he brought with him several live specimens which wriggled around the studio for the benefit of the cameras. The following day a deputation of cleaning ladies came to see the studio manager, threatening to go on strike. One of their number had been swilling down a concrete floor, but found the water unusually reluctant to flow away down the drain pipe set in the wall. The lady herself found the experience too distressing to describe but, according to her spokesperson, she had bent down to examine the blockage, and finding no apparent reason for it assumed the pipe was blocked. She sluiced down a bucketful of water, and went outside to see the result. Then, said the spokesperson, a bloody great eel shot out of the drainpipe and went wiggling round and round the grille, causing the lady severe stress. What was the floor manager going to do about it? What the floor manager did do was to send the cleaning ladies home, in case the technicians got to hear about the incident and came out in sympathy.'

'On the other hand, eels do have their uses,' said Roger Ballantyne, 'as an offensive weapon of psychological warfare. My sister had a boyfriend of whom I and the chap she subsequently married heartily disapproved; my mother approved of him mainly because he would in due course inherit a peerage. He came to stay at home. We put an eel — it was a dead one — in his bed, and then went to spend the weekend elsewhere. I think my sister still blames that eel for the fact that she is not now addressed as Your Ladyship.'

I am writing this story from memory, but the conversation which I have put together as best I can remember it will, I hope, indicate that there was only one person present that evening prepared to champion the cause of the European eel — except to eat — and he was Josh Brandon. However, when we had listened to him, we all had to admit a new respect for the creature.

Josh Brandon continued. 'If you're interested I'll tell you a little more about the eel, because its life history is one of nature's wonders of contrivance, and few people, even if they have seen what Jane saw today, think beyond what a nasty creature it is.

'In Izaak Walton's day several theories were put forward as to how eels spawned. They were never seen to spawn, and elvers appeared in large numbers suddenly. One theory was that dew falling on the banks of ponds or rivers ("Apted by nature for that end" as Walton puts it) during the months of May or June was warmed by the sun and turned into eels, the offspring of Jove, according to some of the ancients. It was not until 1922 that a Danish biologist, by the name of Johannes Schmidt, traced the European eel's spawning ground to the seaweedy eastern side of the Sargasso Sea. He did so after twenty-five years spent laboriously backtracking the diminishing size of eel larvae from their first discovery near the Faroe Islands.

'From the Sargasso Sea, a mass of floating seaweed which you will not find marked on many atlases — it is in fact just to the east of the Bermudas — millions of eel larvae, only about five millimetres long, radiate out in all directions. Only those caught up in the Gulf Stream survive to reach European shores. Almost within sight of land the structure of the larva changes. A drifting wisp of plasma, which has been carried nearly four thousand miles, turns into a live creature, the glass-eel or elver. These elvers pack together in shoals to form a dense column stringing along for miles — eel-fare, hence the name elver — as they enter their favourite European rivers.

'What I find particularly interesting is that over countless centuries the growth of eel larvae has apparently been conditioned by the drifting apart of the continents, the eels holding fast to their earliest spawning grounds and their home rivers, despite the increasing length of the journey involved between the two.' As if he felt he had been hogging the conversation again, Josh paused and took a sip of his coffee.

'I can't say I have ever thought much about how eels get to the places where you find them,' I said, 'for a long time I believed that the spawn got carried to some remote pool on the legs of visiting waterfowl. I knew eels could travel overland if there was sufficient moisture about. Then somewhere or another I read about them breeding in the Sargasso Sea, but it didn't strike a vibrant chord in my imagination that the eels there in that pond had come from the other side of the Atlantic. Incredible when you do come to think about it.

'Incredible, too, that the eels in your pond will leave and make their way back to the other side of the Atlantic, to spawn and die. That is, if they ever get there. So far a fair proportion of them have withstood the attention of herons and other predators, let alone small boys with worm-baited hooks. The heron, incidentally, has a special technique for dealing with eels. He stabs, he holds, and he shakes with a beak specially ridged for the purpose of dealing with slimy fish, then he stabs again before eventually swallowing the wriggling remains. Otters, when they were more common, used to make quite a dent in the eel population of the rivers. But by far the most savage reaper of mature eels on their way back to the sea, silver eels they are called at this stage of their development, are the commercial fisheries. I don't know if there are any commercially run eel-weirs left in this country, but there certainly used to be. It is on the Continent that they go in for harvesting the eels in a big way. At Commachio on the River Po a thousand tons of eels have been caught in a single night.

'During the making of that documentary, we went to East Anglia to talk to some of the old fenmen who had supplemented their weekly wages by catching eels. According to Izaak Walton in *The Compleat Angler*, "In England there is an island called Ely, by reason of the innumerable number of eels that breed in it". True or false I don't know. Certainly Ely was an island in the seventeenth century, a mound surmounted by its glorious cathedral, in the midst of waterlogged fen. When the land was drained two centuries later, the eels remained in the countless levels and dykes constructed for the purpose. And the fenmen knew how to catch them. Traps were woven from osiers in the shape of a champagne bottle. At the base, where the concave indentation is on the bottle, the osiers were laid to form an inward-pointing cone with an open end just large enough to admit an eel in search of the bait inside the trap. When it tried to get out again, the eel could not find the narrow end of a funnel where the sharpened points of the osiers converged. The trap was baited with the handiest form of offal, anchored, and laid in the waterway overnight. The captured eels were emptied out from the stoppered neck of the trap the following morning.'

'I don't know why they wanted to go to all that trouble to make an eel trap,' said Roger Ballantyne. 'When I was a boy the gardener at home showed me a much easier way of making one. Get hold of a sack, put a brick or large stone in it, and some bait wrapped up in muslin − guts, bits of fish, liver, any kind of offal. Stuff the sack full of straw, not too tightly but stuff it full. Then get hold of a section of land-drain, a foot or so long and three inches in diameter. Tie the end of the sack tightly round one end of the land-drain and attach a floating marker so that you can find where you have sunk your trap. In the evening drop the whole caboodle in the river, mouth of the drain pointing downstream during the summer months so that the smell of the bait is wafted along with the current; upstream in the autumn when the eels are migrating down river. The eels nose up the section of land-drain to get at the bait, but they don't seem to be able to find the mouth of the drain to get out again. The straw, as well as filling out the sack, stops other fish from entering. Come and collect in the morning. Not very professional looking, but it works.'

After this interruption Josh Brandon continued. 'Another unconventional method of catching eels is by sniggling, or dibbing for them. There are other names for the process in different parts of the country. A length of line, long enough to reach the bottom when swung out over the water, is tied to the end of a long withy. At the end of the line, eighteen inches of rough worsted, thread is attached. The next, and rather unpleasant, process is to thread worms from end to end the length of the worsted, which is then gathered together to form a gob of worms.

'The catcher with his sniggling kit goes out by night, preferably a moonlight night, to his favourite eel water. The

48

gobbet of worms, suitably weighted, is slung out and left there for an eel to discover. When a tug is felt at the end of the line, with one smooth motion the eel is lifted clear of the water and swung inland before it has time to disentangle its teeth from worm and worsted; if it lands on the bank it will quickly be back again in the water, so the sniggler has another item of equipment with him, a depository for the sniggled eels; an umbrella, we were told, was ideal for the purpose. According to our informant, an old weatherbeaten fenman, if the eels are on the move you can pull them out one after another, and you do not have the problem of removing the hook each time.'

'It's a messy and time-consuming business trying to get the hook out of an eel,' said Roger Ballantyne, 'impossible in the dark, I should imagine. In my limited experience, when I have been worming for trout, the only way to deal with an eel if you want to keep it is to come provided with some newspaper. As soon as you're pretty sure you've hooked one get it on the bank as fast as you can without using your landing- net, or it will cover the net in slime. Once on the bank, put a sheet of newspaper down, and manoeuvre the hooked eel on to it. That properly sticks it, and you can cope. How you cope wouldn't have appealed to your viewers, Josh, but the best answer is to cut-off the hook, kill the eel by snicking it with a knife behind the head, and wrap the result in more newspaper so that it doesn't contaminate your fishing bag.'

'If you made too good a job of killing the eel by the method you suggest,' retorted Josh Brandon, 'you would have a hell of a job skinning it according to the way we were shown: anchoring the eel by nailing it through the head; cutting around the skin beneath; and rolling it off like a glove. A bit difficult if the head comes away when you start pulling off the skin. Having watched the process done very professionally, and seen the cut-up pieces of eel still jerking around afterwards, we decided not to show that on film either for fear of upsetting the restaurant trade.'

'I remember seeing a TV programme once,' I said, 'where

some old boy reckoned the only way to kill an eel properly was to bury it in a shallow grave shaped like a crucifix, and even then it wouldn't die until sunset. Of course, I don't believe it, but he obviously did.'

'I imagine that killing eels was the least of the fenmen's problems; in fact they got a better price for them live, but it wasn't something that cropped up in the making of our film. There is still a lot we do not know about the eel, and where there's mystery there's bound to be superstition.'

Josh added, 'A very versatile creature the eel, apart from the edible quality of the flesh, the skin worn as a bracelet is said to be a cure for rheumatism, and weight for weight it is about the toughest skin you can get. It was once used for making whips, and for joining together the two sections of a threshing flail.'

At that point our talk turned to other matters.

So why should I remember this conversation so well? Most of us, I suppose, have a compartment in our mind labelled 'Personal and Confidential', in which we lock away our pet hates in case other people discover them and laugh at us. How the contents get there I do not know, but once in place, these personal dislikes stay put; skeletons to frighten – and also to fascinate. Some we confess to, some we do not. Contact with an eel is a personal dislike to which I will readily confess. But tell me something new about the eel, or any other one of my pet horrors, and I cannot resist listening, fascinated. It is like listening to a ghost story but not wanting to see a ghost.

It did also strike me, having heard what Josh Brandon had to say, that the common eel is much underrated, deserving a greater degree of recognition. I am not suggesting that such an unattractive creature is likely to inspire the creative writer. In most fishing books eels are dismissed in less than half a dozen pages, if they feature at all. The *Concise Oxford Dictionary* limits itself to, 'A snake-like fish'. Look up eels in the *Guinness Book of Records* and the only entry you will find is of a species which claims the record of being 'the most electric fish', capable of discharging a shock sufficient to kill a person twenty feet away. Fortunately, few of us are likely to encounter the electric eel, which is found in South American waters. Only in cookery books, dead and skinned, does the European eel feature regularly.

There must be countless pictures of leaping salmon and rising trout. But how many have you ever seen of an eel undulating through the water? The only one I recall was on a set of fish plates given to us as a wedding present. All but two of them, including the one with the eels on it, are now broken. Nasty neglected eel, skulking in the mud of a pond, or clinging to the river bed, yet capable of that last momentous journey back down to the sea, to cross the Atlantic Ocean. And the return of its young to the pond or river which it left. But do they? I mean, do the elvers return to the same pond or river?

You will have gathered that my practical experience of eels has been restricted to avoiding contact with them, even to the extent of never fishing with a worm-baited hook (I hate threading the worm on the hook as well) for fear of having to cope with an eel. But I am the first to admit that what the creature lacks in attraction it makes up for in mystery.

I remembered something I had heard when I lived down south. There was a pond near the village where the local lads used to go fishing. Reg, one of them, told me word got round one year that there were really big eels in that pond, and for a time they caught some monsters. Then the eels completely disappeared. 'They say as eels can travel overland,' said Reg. 'I reckon the eels what were in that pond knew that weren't a right place for 'em and moved on elsewhere.' I don't suppose Reg's notion of 'moving on elsewhere' took in the compass of the Caribbean; his knowledge of natural history was limited to what he had seen for himself and what he had learnt from his father and his grandfather, supplemented more recently by some of the nature programmes on the television.

How eels first found that pond at the end of Tithe Barn Lane, or any other landlocked water, is an even bigger mystery than how a salmon homes in on the river of its birth.

But find it they did. So how come new generations failed to return? As a result of the conversation that evening, I thought I had a clue, several clues in fact. Perhaps the locals caught them all, in which case there would have been no survivors to make the final migration from the pond, down the ditch, into the river, the estuary, and out into the Atlantic to the Caribbean. The pond might have become polluted, but why then were the local lads still going there to catch other fish? Or perhaps adult eels had made it back to the Sargasso Sea after all, and their offspring were not lucky enough to get picked up by the Gulf Stream. On the other hand, could it be that Reg was right and the eels avoided the place because somehow they knew, 'That weren't a right place for 'em'? Clues yes, but solution no.

# Chapter Six

## *Un Poisson d'Avril*

I wish I had kept a fishing diary, but I never have. Days that a cue would have prompted me to recall have been forgotten. Only the quirks of memory serve to remind me of special occasions when something was good, or bad, or just different. But so many days which I have enjoyed have been lost in the particulars. Of course I remember my first salmon, everybody does. And when I caught ten in an afternoon — any competent fisherman could have done so in the same circumstances — what I remember best is carrying them all the half mile back to the Lodge. The fish lost, too: the one I snatched at with a gaff, leaving the salmon to swim free, and the gaff, a borrowed one, at the bottom of a deep dark pool. Videos in the mind's eye, to which, with the aid of a recorder, I would like to have added.

I remember a salmon, caught on the 1st of April, the earliest that I have ever caught one in the Struie, a good reason amongst others why I remember the date. The river at Balmeanie was bare of salmon at that time of year, and courtesy of the riparian owner, I was fishing just above where the Struie enters the Kyle, a riverscape of gravel and grass in contrast to the rocks and heather higher up. The salmon came with the tides, some staying, some returning to the salt water to await more favourable conditions for their journey up river.

I have a picture in my mind's eye now of that salmon at the end of my line jumping clear of the water, a silver crescent, a symbol of spring, heralding a river come alive again, released from the cold grip of the Highland winter.

That evening, my cousin Guy Lewis was coming to stay with us on his way up to fish the Helmsdale.

The next day being a Sunday, Guy and I went for a walk up the river, chatting where two could walk abreast along the uphill path, until the going gets rougher when you reach the Falls O' Meanie. Here we stopped. Guy lit his pipe, more I sensed from habit after saving the breath for walking, than for the prospect of reflective enjoyment. The fickle sunshine lit the glen but did little to warm it; clouds in the west gave a hint of some sharp shocks to come before the season of spring finally arrived. Guy wandered off to look at the head of the falls, and I gazed down from the steep bank on the dark water of that familiar pool.

Though there wasn't a salmon to be seen in the pool, there soon would be, lying in serried ranks where the white water ended in frothy bubbles, ready to have a go at the impossible ascent. Now the fall of water was fuelled gradually by the melting snow from the hills; soon it would come down warmer, but then often too little or too much. Too little and the salmon, huddled round the falling stream at the neck, would die from lack of oxygen, too much and they would have to ride out the force of the current at the tail, or drop back out of the pool altogether. The cruellest deception was when the fish instinctively knew that the flow of water over the falls was right for them to run and gain their freedom. You could see them, head above water, sizing up the difficulties of their escape route. Then the leap into the cauldron, the vibrating struggle up the spout of water, the pause half way in the seething pot in the rock face — for those that made it that far — and failure. I hated to see the tumbling floundering bodies knocked off balance and flung back into the pool by the current of water hitting them in the flank as they made the final leap for freedom.

I wondered if there were any survivors from last autumn's run left in the depths. A rocky Highland river like the Struie presents all manner of problems for a spawned salmon, a kelt, hoping to return to the sea, to feed once again, and to restore the ravages of ascending the river and reproducing. Exhausted and wasted in body, the unfortunate fish is once more tumbled by the currents down the rocky path back to the sea, and a fresh chance to live. Many do not survive the journey. In the less rumbustious rivers of the Borders and the south they have a better chance.

A cloud cut off the supply of sunshine and I shivered. What a contrast with yesterday, when catching the fresh-run salmon had symbolised the coming of spring. Yesterday was the 1st of April; in France they call an April fool *un poisson d'avril*. Maybe that fish had made an April fool of me. Spring was not here yet.

I was aroused from these thoughts by the reappearance of Guy Lewis. 'You look a bit solemn,' he said. 'With a setting as beautiful as this outside your front door, the run of your rod on the river, and the salmon on the way up, you ought to be full of the joys of spring.'

'Oh I don't know,' I said. 'Sometimes when you've got it all on your doorstep and you can fish whenever you feel like it, you get to thinking these salmon have a difficult enough time as it is, so why should I add to their problems by luring them to their death with a few feathers tied round a hook.'

'Perhaps it's a better way to go with a ten-minute fight and a sharp tap on the head, than hanging about getting stale as a kipper, and a pretty remote chance of making it back to the sea again. Anyway, a fish may be one of God's creatures but its life is governed by instinct, not emotion, and you can't measure its pleasures and problems in human terms.'

'Maybe not its pleasures Guy,' I said, 'but you can certainly measure its problems, on this river anyway. Let's get back for lunch.'

I led on down the narrow path, and Guy followed.

As the path broadened out into a track we walked abreast again, 'I don't know about you,' Guy said, 'but I get the feeling I'm regarded as a bit of a nut by some people for being a dedicated fisherman. They look at me tolerantly and say, "I'd find it such a dull occupation dangling a line in the water all day in the hope of catching a fish. What on earth do you think about all the time you spend there by the river?" I say "catching fish", which is a good enough answer for someone who is convinced that I'm the fool at one end of the line with the fish at the other. But I don't think people who haven't tried it realise how fishing takes you through the run of your emotions without any damaging after-effects.'

'If you lived up here all the year round with the river to watch like the trees in your garden, Guy,' I said, 'you might find one of the emotions you experienced was pity, not pity for the fresh-run fish you catch, full of fitness and fight, but pity for the unfortunates who waste away, destroyed by the very river to which they return.'

'Hence your sombre mood this morning?'

'Yes, I suppose so, it's just that sort of day. Many years ago, before I had the faintest idea I'd ever come to live in a place like this, I went up to the Borders, stayed in a hotel and fished the local ticket water hoping for a successor to the first two salmon I'd ever caught. It was about this time of year. I flogged away for two or three days without a touch. Then one morning I got into a fish. It milled around without showing, and all I could think of was that there was a salmon at the end of my line. I got it on the bank. I'd landed my salmon, that was all that mattered. An old boy, who seemed to be the doyen of the fishermen in the hotel, happened to walk down to the pool and saw the fish I was so proud of having caught lying there. "Damned kelt," was all he said. When he had gone, I sneaked off and shoved my salmon down a rabbit burrow.'

'Why?' said Guy.

'What d'you mean, why?'

'Why did you shove that kelt down a rabbit burrow?'

'Because I was feeling ashamed I suppose. I don't know,' I said.

'Exactly, and now that you can go and fish whenever you want, waiting until conditions are exactly right, you can afford to be more philosophical.'

Needled by this cross-examination I said huffily, 'It's not a question of being philosophical, just a little bit thoughtful. What on earth are you getting at, Guy?'

'Oh, nothing,' he replied. 'Maybe I'm the one that ought to be feeling a bit guilty over something I've just done. Trying to lay off some of my guilt on you, I suppose.'

We walked the rest of the short way back to the lodge in silence. Guy Lewis left after lunch.

The following evening Ernest Cantrell telephoned. I knew he was up fishing on the Tay, Guy told me he had arranged this for him. Did I know the address of the hotel where Guy was staying, Ernest asked? I supplied the necessary information and enquired how he was getting on. Ernest said he had caught one fish so far. We chatted for a little and he rang off.

I thought no more about the events of that Sunday until six weeks later. I had to go to London, and instead of coming straight back again after the 650-mile journey, I went on to stay with Guy Lewis for the weekend. The north of Scotland seemed very remote from the cosy Hampshire village, set in a hollow amidst the rolling downs, where Guy lived. A picture postcard of rural England it looked, the neat well-manicured houses, the church with its flag of St George stirred by the soft breeze, the village pub jarring the eye only with its sunshades rising over the outside tables like unhealthy toadstools. What a contrast to the wildness of our scenery. And what a contrast to the white and grey sprawl of Bettybridge, with its main street mixture of shops, guesthouses, and bars, its granite kirk, and Fraser's Hotel.

And thinking of Fraser's Hotel, I had to tell Guy the story I had heard there when I went to collect our supplies last week.

A Scottish TV team had been up to interview an old man on his ninetieth birthday who had spent the greater part of his life as a ghillie on one of the nearby hotel waters. 'You must have had some interesting experiences during your time as a ghillie?' the bright young interviewer suggested to him.

'No many,' the old man replied. (This was how the story was told me in Fraser's by one of the locals.)

'People then, you must have met some interesting people?' the interviewer persisted.

'Some was more interestin' than ithers.'

Realising that he was not going to get much out of the old man by such direct questions, the interviewer switched to a more oblique approach. 'I've been told,' he said, 'that when an angler catches his first salmon, as well as giving his ghillie an extra big tip, they have a dram together in the hotel bar afterwards. I bet you must have had quite a few drams on the anglers you've helped catch their first fish. One of the perks of the game isn't it?'

'I dinna ken what ye mean by a perrk, and salmon fishin' is no a game. It's a sport for them as can afford it. Forbye I dinna drink sperrits.'

Used to interviewing sportspersons who were happy to spill out their life-stories of success and hard times at the smallest excuse, the interviewer for once realised that he was getting nowhere with this dour old man of the river. Conscious of the cameras rolling, of his producer's rough tongue for failure to exert his assertive skills, he went on the offensive. 'Oh come on, Mr Cameron, there must be something that sticks out in your mind after the years you've spent by the riverside with all those people. Can't you find anything to tell the viewers?'

'Well, there's just the one wee story that comes to mind,' said the old man.

The cameras switched from Mr Cameron's immobile face to the flexible features of the interviewer, who was now smiling brightly at having got the old boy to talk at last. 'I'm sure our viewers would like to hear that,' he said. The cameras focused back again on the ghillie.

'I seen the gentleman I had wi' me that day, wi' his rod bent, and him shoutin' "Cameron, Cameron, I'm intae a salmon". It was early in the season, and we was on the lower beat where there's plenty o' slack water. There were no many salmon up, an' I thought mebbe it was a pike the gentleman had at the end o' his line. Ye ken the difference between a salmon and a pike?'

'I'm not a fisherman myself, but I'm sure all our angling viewers will know the difference,' said the television man. 'It must have been an exciting moment, though.'

'There's no much excitement wi' a pike on the end o' your line, or wi' a kelt for the matter o' that, and for all the fuss the fisher was making, I guessed by the set o' the rod it had to be the one or th'ither. It turned oot to be a pike. But when it was on the bank an' I'd fetched it a good crack on the head — a pike's verra difficult to kill — the gentleman seemed pleased enough wi' his fish. But he kep' askin' me was I sure it was deid.'

The old ghillie's wee story, extracted from him with such practised skill, was not coming up to expectations. The interviewer decided he must either bring it to a close or get at the human side of this tale about a pike, whatever sort of fish that might be. And he did not like the callous way the ghillie was talking about killing the fish, nor, he suspected, would many of the viewers; experience had taught him that violence was acceptable only when inflicted on people. He would have one more attempt at getting something more interesting and less controversial out of the old man before ending the interview. Soothingly, he addressed his viewers through Mr Cameron, and the cameras obediently picked up the smiling face of the man from Scottish Television. 'I'm sure our viewers would share the concern of the angler that the fish was quite dead if it was not going to be put back in the water again,' he gushed. 'Now would you care to tell them how the story ended.'

On cue, the television cameras switched back to the unsmiling face of Cameron the ghillie, the blue eyes in the craggy red face held steady on the lens.

'I was going tae if you hadnae interrupted,' he growled. Then a discernible twinkle lit up for a moment the intensely blue eyes. 'O' course yon pike's deid, I told the gentleman. And I slit the fush up the belly from the vent to the gills, an' damme, there was a duck sittin' on half a dozen eggs.'

On this visit to Guy and Jane Lewis I was on my own. Ann had not thought it worth coming south just for three days, with me occupied in London for one of them. So after dinner, coffee, and the news on television, Jane Lewis, deprived of feminine gossip, departed for bed, leaving Guy and me to the usual pattern of our first evening together.

Now was my opportunity to tell him about old Cameron's TV interview. When I had finished, and Guy had shown his appreciation of the story with his laughter, he said 'And now I've got something I've been keeping for you.

'Do you remember that Sunday we walked up to the Falls O' Meanie together, and you told me about the kelt you'd caught when you first started fishing, and were so ashamed of killing that you shoved it down a rabbit burrow? You didn't know it, but you made me think in rather a different perspective of something I'd just done. By the way, did you by any chance get a telephone call from Ernest Cantrell the evening I left?'

I said that I had. Ernest had wanted to know where he was staying.

'I thought so,' said Guy. 'After breakfast on the Monday I arrived at the hotel, I went out to meet my ghillie. We introduced ourselves, and he said, "There's a fish [he didn't call it a salmon] arrived for you from the station, Sir". On the slab where the bag was laid out to be admired, was the meanest-looking kelt I've ever seen, tarnished and thin as an eel. Tied around its tail was a label with my name on it, followed by just two capital letters, RD.

' "We had to open the fish bass, Sir," explained the ghillie, "it was sent to the hotel, and marked, Open on Arrival." He looked at me knowingly, "I'm thinkin' yon fush has done more than its fair share o' travellin' alive and deid. Will I gie it a decent burial?"

'I said yes and thanked him, at the same time putting two and two together in my mind to make precisely four. I should have known that Ernest Cantrell usually had the last laugh.'

Guy paused at this point, the flow of his story diverted by

some thought which seemed to have struck him. He said, 'I know it's maddening when a person is telling you something that happened, and breaks off in midstream, leaving you up in the air. But that's what I'm going to do. You'd much better hear the beginning of the story from Ernest himself; it began with him and it ended with him. Besides, I've got a selfish motive as well, I'd love to hear what he's got to tell you. Can you wait to hear the rest from him, he'll be up with you in about a month's time, won't he?'

I said he would, and with that I had to be content.

In the event I had no reason to ask Ernest what had happened that first week in April when he had been up fishing on the Tay. He told me himself. The story came out like this.

'You remember the night I telephoned you a couple of months ago to find out the hotel where Guy was staying? I told me I'd caught a fish, didn't I?' The three of us, Ernest, Ann and I, were sitting drinking our coffee after dinner. Ernest spoke more as a prosecutor opening his case than as a story-teller. He singled me out as his witness, leaving Ann to the unbiased rôle he apparently saw for her as a member of the jury. He said, 'Well, there's a bit of a story to that particular fish, and you'd better hear it.

'When I got down to the beat I'd been allocated that first morning, I took one look at the river. The current swept past me from bank to bank, fast-moving and featureless. I could not have thrown a cricket ball from one side to the other. God, I thought to myself, where do I put my fly and how do I get it there? Then the ghillie appeared; I hadn't noticed him, my attention had been occupied by the river. He took charge of my gear and led me down to what I had not been expecting, a boat.

'I remember seeing a rod already made up lying over the stern of the boat, with a large landing-net beside it. I didn't think anything particular of it at the time, just noticed the rod at my first glance round the boat without wondering what it was doing there. My main concern was how one man was going to handle this solid-looking craft in that current.

61

'The next five or ten minutes was taken up with the ghillie's inspection of my fishing equipment. He muttered over the frailty of my rod, reel, line, and cast; took one look at my fly and removed it with his pocket knife, replacing it with a miniature meathook, all tinsel and dyed feathers, taken from a tobacco tin in his pocket. He then instructed me to sit on a thwart across the blunt bows, and pushed off, heaving himself aboard as the boat caught the thrust of the current. With a grunt he settled himself amidships, took up the oars, and presented me with his broad back. I thought I would have been a great deal better off in the stern.

'I've never fished such a featureless stretch of water, and fished it with what felt like a lump of lead attached to the end of my line. Salmon there might be lying in the depths, but neither the sight of one, nor any reassurance as to their presence from the ghillie, encouraged me to believe that the enormous fly in which I had little faith probed anything but an empty river bed.

'And the effort involved in getting that damned fly out into the flow of water running dark and deep a foot or two beneath the pivot of my bottom on the hard thwart! Each time I dragged it clear of the water, my rod flexed its utmost to get the beastly thing airborne and fling it out again; my twelve foot of carbon fibre was simply not strong enough to cope. On several occasions the wretched lure, I should not dignify it with the name of fly, either failed to take off and I had to abort the cast, or it hit the water behind and whirred uncomfortably close overhead on the return journey.

'It may have been my casting, or it may have been other considerations which I was about to discover, that caused the ghillie to hold the boat steady in the diminishing current – we were now nearly out in the broad pool which it fed – and for the second time that morning to give me the benefit of his advice. "Yon winkle-pick of a rod," he said, "is no man enough for the job. You'd best try this yin." And he handed me the rod in the stern.

'The rod I now had hold of was a sturdy greenheart pole,

fourteen foot or so long, the sort they made fifty years ago, and heavy. What it would be like to cast with I dreaded to think, then I noticed that half the reel line was in the water. In handing me the rod the ghillie had not offered any explanation for this, and since I found myself once again facing only the thick red neck between cap and coat, I did not think it was worth asking for one.

'I reeled in the slack line. Then I met resistance. At first I thought the fly was stuck fast in the river bed. With my finger against the spool of the reel I gave a jerk, but it did not come free. Whatever it was attached to moved, and continued to move, stripping more line off against the ratchet. Could there be a fish there? The answer was to put on more strain and see. I had been told that spring salmon tend to be sluggish in the cold water.

'I noticed the ghillie glance over his shoulder, take in the bend of my rod, and start rowing towards the bank. I didn't attempt to recover line against the drag of the current and the motion of the boat until we grounded on the shingle. Then stepping ashore I began to reel up. No ordinary salmon could be this sluggish.

'I continued to reel in. The ghillie, unable to ignore my presence any longer on the pretext of piloting the boat, would surely be forced to acknowledge some interest in whatever it was at the end of my line. Now it was my turn to look over my shoulder at him. He was standing with his eyes fixed on the point where the line entered the water. I looked there too, and saw a shape being dragged along the bottom. It was a fish all right, but it looked to me like a dead fish. I said to the ghillie, "Aren't you going to land it for me?" Without comment he went over to the boat, picked up the landing-net, came back, and slipped it under the fish, which I could now see was quite dead.

'We both bent over. I had never seen a kelt before. I was seeing one now. The ghillie kneeled on the shingle to remove the fly, and straightening up again, without a word handed me a small plastic envelope sealed along the top, and punctured above the seal where it had been impaled on the fly. There was a label inside. Pencilled on it were the words "April Fool" .'

In the pause which Ernest allowed for his words to sink in, Ann spoke. 'But Ernest, it must have been a put-up job involving the ghillie,' she said. 'How else could it have been organised?'

'Of course, the ghillie did the donkey work. Who else could have done so without the local knowledge? He was the obvious person to set up the leg-pull, and see it through,' replied Ernest. 'What he did not know was how it would go down. The joke could easily have backfired on him; he knew that too, and it worried him. But whoever had put him up to it obviously had a good deal of clout. That much I put together after reading the "April Fool" message.

'The unfortunate ghillie — his name was Jimmy Watt, I got on well with him later — had no idea how I would react. I can look pretty po-faced when I want to. I told him to take the kelt and put it in the larder (which I doubt if he did), drove back to the hotel on my own, and let him stew for the rest of the day.

'I had my suspicions about who was responsible for nobbling the ghillie, and they were limited to two people. That evening I telephoned you.

'The next morning I saw Jimmy Watt and told him that I would forget about yesterday's little episode, and not mention it to anyone or write and complain about it, if he would follow my instructions exactly. I have no doubt that you know the rest.'

Then as an afterthought — or was it the whole purpose of his telling me this story? — Ernest Cantrell added, 'I assume it was Guy Lewis to whom I should have sent that kelt?'

# Chapter Seven

# Fair Means and Foul

'On high the dazzling blaze to rear,
And heedful plunge the barbèd spear'

Those lines of Sir Walter Scott's always bring the same picture
to mind. I close my eyes and the scene comes to life. The dead
of night, the muttering current of a broad river, and a boat
outlined in the lambency of a blazing torch held aloft by a man
in the bows; the rest of the crew, bearded and bonneted,
armed with leisters – tridents for spearing fish – peering into
the water intent on seeing the shape of a salmon attracted to
the surface by the light. They called it Burning the Water.

The very words, Burning the Water, are emotive enough,
and Sir Walter Scott's description (which he surely witnessed
himself on the Tweed) takes you back nearly two centuries to
imagine what it must have been like, this weird hunt to spear
salmon to feed hungry bellies. Poaching, like smuggling, has
always been at the glamour end of the crime business.

But I defy anyone to glamorise poisoning the water, carried
out today by a different class of poacher altogether. Hunger or
a few bob in an empty pocket is no longer the motive, but
naked greed for cash regardless of the consequences.

Cymag is a chemical derivative of cyanide; released in a
river it kills underwater in the same way as cyanide gas kills in
the air. The tainted water deprives fish life of oxygen, and
suffocates every living creature with which it comes in close
enough contact – salmon parr, smolts, trout, eels, the lot. No
skill, no glamour, no consideration, no wonder; this breed of
poacher robs a river because it is safer than robbing a bank.

In between this extreme of poisoning an entire pool and taking edible salmon illicitly, there are many shades of grey. Almost as black as poison is the use of explosive. It is not easy to obtain fuse, detonator and explosive, and even a dull thud can be heard a long way off on a silent night, so the method is not very common. At least the stun effect of an underwater explosion is immediate and does not suffocate like Cymag; besides, only the fish nearest the explosion are killed outright, others merely stunned.

But people who live in glass houses should not throw stones. Or high-explosive. Please do not get me wrong. I have never bombed a river, but I have bombed the sea.

Boredom, curiosity, and the immediate availability of one-pound gun-cotton slabs, primers, detonators, and slow-burning fuse led me to commit this crime. We, that small part of the Army with which I was doing my National Service, were despatched from the Canal Zone of Egypt to the Hashemite Kingdom of Jordan in order to protect British interests from the consequences of an early knockout in the first few rounds of the fight between Arab and Jew. Our presence alone was considered to be sufficient to achieve this purpose; Showing the Flag, it used to be called.

Maybe the antagonists were too busy with their own footwork to take any notice of the immediate presence of some six hundred British soldiers, but they left us well alone. Our military duties were therefore confined to the usual dull routine of guards and patrols, the rest of the time being our own to occupy as we chose. The choice was limited, camped on the edge of a shanty town where the desert meets the sea, a hundred miles from any dwelling other than a huddle of Arab tents. The sea offered more than the sand, let alone the shopless town; at least you could bathe in it. And we heard that there were strange fish beneath the azure surface.

I have always maintained that in fishing, knowledge is more important than skill. When it comes to using high-explosive, knowledge is essential and skill of no consequence whatever. You have to know at what rate safety fuse burns, and to understand the volatile nature of detonators. Otherwise the procedure is simple; insert fuse in detonator, insert detonator in primer and primer in guncotton slab, light fuse, and when it starts fizzing and spitting sparks, throw all into the water.

Wait, while you watch bubbles coming to the surface where you have thrown the explosive. Then comes a deep thud, more felt than heard, and an eruption on the surface of the water. Then up come the fish. Swim in and collect. And what a collection! Not a big bag, but what variety; long fish, short fish, fish of all colours, fish with beaks, and fish with spines — long spines, sharp spines, poisonous spines, as I found out to my cost. After having landed a spiny fish my hand swelled up like a football, and stayed up. A local Arab had the answer — arak. Arak is alcohol, a kind of Pernod or absinthe, rough and very strong. External application with it soon neutralised whatever fishy poison infected my hand.

I have confessed this offence of bombing the sea to a friend of mine, who comes to stay with us at Balmeanie. He says that a similar, but scaled-down, effect to the use of explosives can be achieved on a river by hitting the rock face of a pool a resounding blow with a fourteen-pound sledge-hammer.

Netting is another way of wholesale poaching. The limiting factor used to be the bulk and weight of the net. With the discovery of nylon, and the subsequent by-product of nylon netting, both these factors were removed. Now miles of the stuff are manufactured to be trailed quite legally in the sea, with devastating effect. I suppose the one advantage to the professional poacher of the old hemp netting was that it could be manufactured at home. Where he obtains the nylon equivalent is a well-kept trade secret. Fortunately the penalties nowadays for being caught with a net are extremely tough, especially in Scotland.

Snatching, stroke-hauling, gaffing or cleeking; and for trout, tickling and the otter, are all means of taking fish illegally, especially suited to the individual poacher. Snatching involves the use of a large weighted triangle hook at the end of a strong line. Drag the triangle across the salmon lies, especially in low water, and sooner or later a fish is foul-hooked. Stroke-hauling is the Irish equivalent of snatching. The gaff is a handy weapon in the hand of an expert for extracting salmon from pots and crannies in the rock face on their way up a steep watercourse, or anywhere else where they can be seen close enough to the surface of the water and to the bank. Cleeking is the Scottish equivalent of gaffing. You hear a lot about tickling, which involves getting your hand under a trout, stroking its belly, and then, when it is lulled into a false sense of security by the gentle motion of your fingers, scooping it out on to the bank. I have yet to meet the person who has either done it, or seen it done. An otter is a device which, when towed along the bank, carries a line with lots of droppers and flies attached to it out into a loch to attract the attention of the maximum number of trout.

So much for the methods. What about the poachers? The only poacher I know up here is Kenny Forbes, and I couldn't prove a thing against him, except one indictment of which he was proven guilty, not by me or by any court of law, but by my predecessor, Kenneth Bunbury. Kenny's method of poaching, which might not be strictly so defined within the confines of the law, but of which he was found guilty, was more sophisticated than the use of 'any light, wire or snare, spear, gaff or snatch, or stones or other missiles', as specified in the Game Laws.

Kenneth Bunbury was, until he became a landed proprietor in the Highlands of Scotland, a partner in a prosperous firm of London stockbrokers, and even when he came to live at Balmeanie, he spent a good deal of his time in London looking after the interests of his former clients; especially where those interests coincided with his own. At such times Balmeanie Lodge was cared for by the housekeeper, and the fishing on the river by the ghillie engaged by Kenneth Bunbury. His name: Kenny Forbes.

One evening, Bunbury was having a drink at his club in London when a man came in whom he knew but had not seen for a long time. The conversation must have gone something like this.

Kenneth Bunbury: 'Hello, Tony, haven't seen you for ages. How are you, come and have a drink.'

Friend: 'I'm not in London much these days, one of the advantages of semi-retirement. But you don't live in London either, do you? I heard you'd bought some place in the north of Scotland.'

The conversation proceeds as you might expect between two men who know one another, but who have not met for some time, then...

Friend again: 'Matter of fact, I was up in your part of the world last year, fishing. I went up there to prospect, find some fishing I could take on a regular basis. I stayed in a place called Bettybridge. D'you know it?'

Kenneth Bunbury, treading warily: 'Yes. I expect you stayed in Fraser's, it's the only reasonable hotel in Bettybridge.'

Friend: 'That's the place. The Glentore Estate office is in the town, if you could call it that. I planned on seeing the factor the day after I arrived to find out if the estate had got any fishing available. But that evening I had a stroke of luck. I went into the hotel bar for a drink before dinner; the place was pretty empty and I got talking to the barman. He asked me if I was up there for the fishing. I said I was up looking for fishing. He said there was a chap in the other bar who was a ghillie, it might be worth my while having a word with him.'

Kenneth Bunbury went on listening. His friend continued. 'Anyway, the upshot was this ghillie offered me a couple of days on the water he was responsible for if I cared to stay on in Bettybridge. He said the owner was away down south, and he was in charge. He often let casual days on behalf of his master who was glad of the extra money when no one was fishing there. We caught two salmon, which cost me fifty quid plus a tenner for the ghillie. Cheap at the price, wasn't it?'

Kenneth Bunbury: 'Very cheap. And I think I know where you caught those two salmon, and the name of the ghillie.'

'How do you know that?'

'I guessed.'

So much for the professionals. What about the amateurs?

According to Jock Robertson, Elsie Bunbury, Kenneth's wife, was as good an amateur poacher as any if she could not catch a salmon by legitimate means. Jock suspected that this was partly due to the unbending attitude of her husband Kenneth, who pontificated to all and sundry about the sanctity of the salmon in his river, and how they should be caught by no other means than the fly.

Elsie must have caught her fair share of salmon on the fly all right, I found the evidence of that. As well as the empty gin bottles we discovered in the cupboard in the rod room, we found behind an old coat hanging on the door a woman's golfing bag. This particular bag contained fishing equipment. There were two fly boxes, one box being full of conventional flies of varying types and sizes appropriate for use on a small Highland river. In the other box there were no compartments or tabs to hold flies in place, just a layer of foam rubber to cover the contents; underneath, a selection of angling ironmongery for use, one might think, on a broad river in early spring. Most of the flies were tied on large double hooks and all were brightly coloured. Thunder and Lightnings with their conspicuous jungle-cock cheeks seemed to be the most popular choice: there were heavy tube flies and a selection of triangle hooks to go with them; plus one or two weirdos, flies with painted metal bodies and flies with miniature propellors attached to them. All in all, a selection made for snatching rather than catching.

I do not doubt that Alec Ross and Elsie Bunbury were partners in crime. Alec told me that one day Kenneth Bunbury had found a jar of worms left on the path beside the Cairns, one of the main holding pools on the river, and sent for him demanding an explanation as to how they got there. 'Worrms in a jar, Sir, are no worrms on the hook. I'm no responsible 'til the worrms get from one to th'ither,' said Alec, according to himself. He added to me, 'I dug 'em up meself for Mrs Bunbury that very morn.' Although Alec was a ghillie, he had all the instincts of a poacher. He needed to catch salmon, and if they could not be caught by fair means, well then, there was always the alternative.

Strictly speaking I do not suppose you can poach on your own water, or your husband's. But poaching is also defined as, 'Capturing [game, fish] by illicit or unsportsmanlike methods', and on this count the circumstantial evidence clearly pointed to Elsie Bunbury's guilt.

Thankfully we do not see much of the professional poachers at Balmeanie. I did have an encounter with one, though. It was during the late afternoon after a lovely spring day in early May. I was fishing the Falls O' Meanie pool and had got to where the current loses itself in the deep water. I had fished out my cast and was reeling up in preparation for the next with my fly coming in fast close to the surface, when I saw the white gleam of something turning in the water close into the bank. At first I thought it was a fish that had followed the fly and was turning away at the last moment, then I saw a white belly replaced by a grey back, a long thick tail, and a stream of bubbles. I never did see the otter come ashore.

The other creature which captures a salmon by unsportsmanlike methods is the grey seal. The seal swims alongside and clouts the fish with a flipper. If you look through polaroid glasses at the serried ranks of salmon as they gather in the Falls O' Meanie pool, as like as not you will see at least one of them with the gash of a seal's claw marking its flank. Put a fly over these fish (not, I may say, with the intention of foul-hooking one of them) and the most likely taker is a wounded one.

I know a small river on the West Coast of Scotland, typical of that area. It drains a loch and flows for about two miles into the sea. The course is not particularly steep, but in places it is rocky and uneven. Once in a while a seal makes its way up the river from the sea, negotiating all the obstacles, to play havoc with the salmon and sea trout in the loch. But it is a one-way journey for the seal.

There is a bit of the poacher in many of us. I hesitate to say most of us because for one thing there are those Pharisees of fishing who are incorruptible, and because I cannot vouch for what goes through someone else's mind when the river is full of fish which assiduously ignore their fly for days on end. Speaking for myself, I confess to being tempted to try something else, not to snare but to persuade, to persuade one of those fish − just one of them − to take an interest in what is tied to the end of my cast. But conscience makes cowards of us all, that, or the fear of being caught doing what you should not be doing.

Now that there is little likelihood of my being caught doing what I should not be doing with a fishing rod in my hands at Balmeanie, I try to remind myself what it was like when I had only a few days, or a fortnight at the most, in which to have the thrill of a salmon at least making a pass at my fly. I have come to the conclusion that there is a great deal of hypocrisy and cant attached to salmon fishing. Kenneth Bunbury seemed prepared to watch salmon dying by the score in the Falls O' Meanie pool for lack of water (and its oxygen content), when a simple pass would have taken them to the pleasant river above; but use a spinner or a bunch of worms in a full spate, never.

A story I heard the other day suggests they still remember Burning the Water in the Highlands. The local midwife was called out in the middle of the night to a croft at the back of beyond. There was no electricity, and she had to sterilise her equipment on the stove. Then, accompanied by the crofter, she went to his wife's assistance. She told him, whether he liked it or not, he would have to hold a torch for her to see what she was doing. The crofter held the torch and the midwife went to work. After the necessary preliminaries, the midwife delivered a child. 'Hold on,' she said to the crofter, 'there's another bairn here.' Child number two was delivered. Still the midwife remained doubled over the heaving, groaning body in the bed. 'Ye're no done yet,' she said, 'there's a third babby.' There was a crash, the room was plunged into darkness, and the crofter's distraught voice exclaimed, 'It's the light that's bringing 'em.'

# Chapter Eight

# A Doctor's Discovery

'The doctor you have dismissed charges against is a disgrace to your profession.' These words were shouted by an enraged local landowner, according to the newspaper I read, from the public gallery at a hearing by the General Medical Council investigating the alleged misdeeds of a Highland GP. Captioned the 'Whisky Galore Doctor', there was a picture of the doctor, bearded, kilted, sporraned and hosed, looking very pleased with himself.

Fourteen of the doctor's patients had come 700 miles to complain, amongst other things, that they had seen him under the influence of drink while on duty. One of them claimed that he chastised her (one wonders whether the chastisement was verbal or physical) because she was 'too bloody fat'.

Other allegations against the 'Whisky Galore' doctor were that he wrongly identified a patient whilst intoxicated, that he had six glasses of whisky on his daily round, and that he drank a glass of whisky before attending to a patient lying unconscious at his feet. The unconscious patient, locally known as Red Pete, had fallen off a stool in the local bar, knocking himself out and cutting his head. The paper did not say whether the doctor was with Red Pete before or after the accident.

The 'Whisky Galore' doctor drives a maroon vintage Bentley in his deerstalker, kilt and sporran, says a lady journalist who once went with him on his rounds, intending to write about a Highland practice. When she witnessed how much he drank, she says, she abandoned the project, believing it would harm the medical profession generally.

According to the newspaper article the doctor refused the offer of a celebratory drink when cleared of all ten charges of professional misconduct, 'as scowling patients milled around.'

My reaction on reading this piece was to wonder why anyone, let alone a doctor, should wish to make such a damn fool of himself dressing up like a bit-part actor in an early Hollywood movie and boozing on duty. I felt very sorry for the patients stuck with this buffoon as their only medical practitioner, and thought how lucky we were with our own universally revered GP. I cut the article out to show him, not that I would have much chance of seeing him in Fraser's Hotel or any other local bar.

Our doctor, James Miller — Doctor Jimmy as he is known locally — qualified at Edinburgh University and practised in England for many years before coming north once again to minister to the scattered community spreading around Bettybridge. He is a man in his middle to late fifties, small, round-faced, balding, and soft-spoken with the faintest trace of a Scottish accent. He wears — it seems almost always — a brown tweed suit, and polished brown shoes which he carries into the house to change into from gum-boots in foul weather; on his head outside he favours a dark brown felt hat instead of a flat cap. He drives around in a red Range Rover, the only vehicle, he says, to get him safely through the winter snows; red for easy spotting, rather expensive, but better than do-it-yourself treatment for hypothermia, he adds. I have got to know him well over the years, but I still call him Doctor when we meet.

Doctor Jimmy's surgery is a modern, purpose-built building in Bettybridge, and he lives in what has always been known as the Doctor's House, a villa which must have been built at the turn of the century standing in its own grounds half a mile outside the town. There is no conveniently placed hospital to which he can easily refer his patients; he makes his own diagnoses, and except in extreme cases prescribes his

75

own treatment. He has the great asset of being able to inspire confidence in his patients; he knows them and they know him as people first and patients or doctor after; he will come out any time and anywhere to visit them in what they may regard as an emergency, and not give them the rough side of his tongue if it turns out to be a false alarm. As a result he is only called out as a last resort. He is a man of many parts. There is no local vet between here and Dingwall, a distance of some twenty-five miles, and I have known Doctor Jimmy to administer an injection of penicillin to an injured dog.

Doctor Miller's only outdoor leisure interests so far as I know are golf and curling. I offered him a day's fishing soon after we came here, but he declined, saying that he liked salmon to eat but he could not be bothered to fish for them. I have no doubt he got quite enough for his kitchen without having to visit the fishmonger's.

Soon after I read the 'Whisky Galore' doctor article, I ran into Doctor Jimmy getting into his Range Rover outside the surgery in Bettybridge. We stopped for a chat. I asked him if he had noticed the piece about the Highland doctor in the papers, rather thoughtlessly, I suppose, because no one likes to see their own profession let down by one of its members. Yes, he had seen the article he said. Then he made just this one comment: 'The General Medical Council may have let him off. His patients won't.'

Soon after that Jimmy Miller telephoned me. Would I do him a favour? he asked. Of course, if I can, I said. He told me he had a friend and ex-colleague coming to stay who was a keen fisherman; could I arrange a day's fishing at Balmeanie for this friend? I readily agreed, and we fixed the date.

Doctor Jimmy brought his friend up to Balmeanie at nine-thirty one morning in early May. He introduced me to Doctor David Morgan from Hay-on-Wye. The two doctors had apparently been partners in a practice in South London before their backgrounds caught up with them. Despite the prosperity of the London practice, they both longed to return to their roots; James Miller to Scotland and David Morgan to the Welsh Borders. Having introduced us, our own doctor drove away, saying he would be back to collect his friend around seven o'clock that evening.

Alec Ross was in attendance on another fishing guest. I told him to keep upstream of Balmeanie Bridge for the morning, and started Doctor Morgan off on the first pool down from there, apologising to him for the lack of a ghillie. I said I would show him where to go, and the most likely lies, then leave him to his own devices. He said that suited him fine; he did not usually fish with a ghillie in attendance, and in fact much preferred being on his own. I had already gathered from Doctor Jimmy that he was an experienced fisherman. We walked to the end of our fishing on the Struie, the pools were obvious enough, and I pointed out the most likely lies in this height of water; I looked through the flies in his fly box, selecting for him what I thought were the best ones to use, and left him, saying I would come and see how he was getting on before lunch. After lunch he could try upstream of the bridge.

At about twelve o'clock I walked down to the river again to find Doctor Morgan. Rounding the bend where the Balmeanie Burn enters the Struie I saw him towards the end of the broad pool called the Fank Pool. His rod was bent and at first I thought he was into a fish. As I got closer, I could see that if it was a fish it was a remarkably sulky one, because the line was not moving from where it entered the water. The doctor tugged hard, obviously against some inert object, but one which moved. So his fly was not snagged on a rock. It must be a waterlogged bough, I thought. The thing at the end of the doctor's line came in more easily now that it was in the slacker water, but the rod remained bent in a steep curve.

Doctor Morgan had remained strangely silent since I had arrived on the scene. Of course, we had only met earlier that morning, but in the present circumstances one might have expected at least some expression of annoyance or frustration on his part. Instead he seemed − how can I put it? − somehow withdrawn. He never glanced in my direction. His face was

77

tense and his eyes fixed on the river in front of him. Now the line met the water some fifteen yards out from the rocky bank on which we were standing. Peering into the depths I could now see something white being dragged slowly towards us. Then I made out the shape. It was a dead sheep.

Doctor Morgan must have seen the drowned sheep at the same time as I did. He pointed his rod straight at it, gave the reel line a vicious tug, the cast parted at the fly, and the line went slack.

The doctor reeled up, and turning to me said, 'Do you mind if we leave this pool and go back upstream?'

As we walked along the path together Doctor Morgan did not say anything, and I, respecting his mood, did not tax him with my conversation until we reached the Castle Pool, which was one of the best on the river. I suggested that he should fish it down before lunch, a good suggestion as it turned out, because at his third or fourth cast he was into a fish. He dealt with the salmon in a very professional manner, and some ten minutes later I netted it for him, a nice clean-run fish, I guessed about eight pounds in weight, average for the Struie.

After the capture of the salmon I left him to his packed lunch, saying I would try to come back in the afternoon, but if I got waylaid I thought he would not find it very difficult to work out for himself the likely lies in the pools above Balmeanie Bridge.

That afternoon I got into various little local difficulties, not the least of which was the early return of the other fishing party, husband and wife, fishless and angry, demanding tea and sympathy because she had hooked a salmon and lost it, blaming Alec Ross for shouting at her and getting her into a tizzy. After tea I suggested a calming walk up the hill with field-glasses to see if they could spot the golden eagle which spent its time robbing me, according to season, of new-born lambs and grouse. Soon after that Doctor Jimmy telephoned to say he had been called out in an emergency and might be late coming to collect David Morgan. Glad of an excuse to be out of the way when the eagle-watching party returned, I offered to drive Doctor Morgan back to Bettybridge, an offer which was gladly accepted.

About six o'clock Doctor Morgan got back to the Lodge. At least he was happy, having caught another fish.

After offering him a drink, which he declined, I gave my guest one of his salmon and we set off in my car for Bettybridge. After we had been going for a few minutes Doctor Morgan said, 'I really must apologise for treating you as if you were not there when I hooked that dead sheep, but the last time I hooked something which felt like that, I got rather a shock.'

'The only thing I noticed,' I said, 'was how restrained you were in the circumstances. I'm one of those people who can't help cursing inanimate objects when they frustrate me. But I'd be interested to hear what happened on the previous occasion, if you'd care to tell me.'

This is what Doctor Morgan told me as we drove to Bettybridge. I did not hurry. I was far too interested in his story.

'Jimmy Miller will have told you that I live and practise in the Hay-on-Wye area. I also have a rod in a syndicate which rents some fishing on the Wye. One afternoon several years ago now – I remember the date: the 17th of March, St Patrick's Day – surgery finished early and I decided to go fishing. It was a raw day with plenty of water in the river. Rather than have the hard work of using a big fly I decided to spin.

'I had fished for an hour or so when my spinner, a big Devon minnow, snagged in something. I pulled hard to free it and whatever the triangle had hooked underwater began moving off downstream, slowly, but with very considerable power. I had no other option but to follow or I would have been broken. I never really thought I was into a fish. I guessed it was some large waterlogged object like the broken-off bough of a tree carried along by the force of the stream. In the shallower water at the tail of the pool the object at the end of my line ceased to move with the current, obviously having come up against a rock or some other obstacle, and I paused to think out the best way to recover my Devon.

'I decided to see if I could get a direct pull from a different angle to free my spinner, and walked downstream to get beneath where my line entered the water before giving a sharp tug. No luck. The submerged bough, which by now I was sure it was, had come to rest some fifteen yards from the bank on my side of the river, and I thought it might be just about possible for me to wade out and see if I could drag it in with my gaff. I propped my rod up on the bank, took hold of the line in one hand, and with the aid of my wading-stick, which doubles as a gaff, in the other, cautiously waded out into the river to get as near as possible to where I thought the sunken bough was. Getting as close as I dared, I gave the line a final sharp tug, but still the spinner stuck fast. Nothing for it now but a sustained pull. The trace I had on was a strong one, so making sure I had as firm a foothold as possible, I twisted the line around my free hand and pulled.

'Now that I was in direct contact, through line and trace, with whatever it was that held my spinner fast, it was as if I was tugging at some dead weight; there was none of the springiness in the pull you usually feel with stretched nylon. I hauled, the line came in a little, I took a turn of it around my hand, and hauled again, at which point I met with soggy resistance which I could shift no further. I tried this two or three times, got fed up and decided that I might as well have one final heave, and if it broke the cast too bad, I had already spent enough time on a two-quid Devon minnow. Rather foolishly, I let go of my wading-stick, which was attached to me by a piece of cord, got both hands on the line, and pulled without thinking what would happen if I overbalanced when the trace parted.

'The trace did not part, but the object moved, and continued to move, very sluggishly. And now I began to wonder if after all it could be a waterlogged bough; I would have felt that bumping on the bottom or against the rocks. To begin with I had just wanted to retrieve my Devon minnow; now I was plain curious to know what on earth I had hooked. I shifted my hold on the line, letting go of it with one hand to reclaim my wading-stick, and my precarious balance. If I can bring this thing into shallower water, I thought to myself, I can fish around with my gaff to see if I can get hold of it.

'Wading a few careful steps backwards, I found a better foothold, and pulled steadily; once more the same sensation of inert resistance to begin with, followed by sluggish movement. But this time I kept on pulling until the line was a direct extension of my arm.

'I couldn't see the bottom, the water was too discoloured. But when I had the line at full stretch I could see something white beneath the surface; when I let go again it went out of sight, subsiding with none of the springiness you would expect of the twigs on a drowned branch.

'I transferred the line to my left hand and, upending the wading-stick so that the gaff end was in the water, took hold of it in my right. I pulled once again. Now peering down I could see the white object but could not make out what it was, and just beneath it the gold body of my Devon fast in something dark-coloured. I sunk the gaff in the water, reaching down as far as I dared, and aiming for the Devon made a grab. The gaff caught hold and I was nearly caught off balance.

'Regaining my foothold, I heaved. What was unmistakably a human hand came to the surface. It was followed by a wallowing body dressed in some kind of military uniform.

'Now do you see why I was a little on edge when you found me before lunch? I remember the sensation only too well of hooking a drowned body, and I wondered what it was this time. Anyway, to return to my story.

'I have been a GP for a good many years, and I've seen a lot of dead bodies, but I'm not a pathologist. I left the corpse, still in the water close to the bank, untouched, and went to the nearest house about quarter of a mile away to telephone the police. I explained who I was, told them what had happened, and said I would stay on the road nearest to the spot where I had fished out the body and wait for the patrol car to come.

'Twenty minutes or so later a police car arrived. I noticed it came from the Welsh side of the border. I led the two constables down to where the body was lying in the water; fortunately no one else had come along that way. Except for identifying me, neither constable had said anything in English so far. The two of them now surveyed the corpse of the drowned soldier with that dead-pan expression of the policeman doing his duty. Then one of them spoke to me; sighing heavily, he said: "You couldn't tow it downstream a bit, Doctor, I suppose? That way it would be in England, and we wouldn't 'ave the bother of it, see."

'The next day I drove to the police station in Brecon to make a formal statement. Being a local doctor, they knew me there. I asked the sergeant if they had managed to identify the body of the drowned soldier, and he told me that the police had been in contact with the nearest military unit, the headquarters of the Special Air Service Regiment in Hereford. Knowing there would have to be an inquest, the SAS had reluctantly admitted that one of their troopers had gone missing some months ago. Since there was no trace of him, either at his home or following searches made of the training areas, they assumed he had gone absent without leave, and after the statutory twenty-one days classified him as a deserter. This was the unfortunate man whose body my Devon minnow had recovered from the river.

'As you know, the SAS maintains its secrecy, as well as its pride. It is to their credit that they sent an officer round to see me. He had the authority to tell me the full story.

'The soldier whose body I had discovered, call him Trooper X, had obviously drowned while on survival training at night. Perhaps the man had missed his footing in the dark and, weighed down with his equipment, been carried away; perhaps he had tried to wade or swim the river – loose clothing equipped with a good number of pockets fills with water as a balloon fills with air, dragging the wearer down and hampering all attempts at swimming. Exactly how he ended up in the River Wye and was drowned will never be known, but clearly he was no deserter.

'According to his officer, Trooper X had a young wife and a small child. Not only had they to face the possibility that husband and father had simply walked out on them for ever, without so much as a word, but they had been denied any financial support from the military authorities on the grounds that the man had been a deserter. Now at least they knew that he had died, still caring for them, while trying to do his job as best he could.

'Sad though the occasion may be, a funeral is the final mark of respect for a life from comrades, friends, family, wife and children. Trooper X was to be given a military funeral.

'The stigma of deserter had been lifted from the late Trooper X. His widow and child could think of him with pride. And they would be entitled to some form of financial assistance still to be worked out. In the meantime the Regiment was looking after the wife of one of its own men.

'Having told me this the officer left. What he had said had given me the consolation of knowing that, in exchange for a most unpleasant experience, I had solved a mystery and mitigated a tragedy.'

We drove on to the Doctor's House, and I left him with the invitation to come and fish again the next time he was up. On the way home I wondered if the 'Whisky Galore' doctor had any interesting stories to tell.

# Chapter Nine

# Hooked

September: and fishing drawing to a close for another year, the water getting colder, the salmon in the pools concerned with what brought them there; they lie in the deeper parts waiting to find a spawning place. If you catch one it will no longer be bright silver, but tarnished, maybe a hen fish gravid with eggs, or a cock developing a kype, the hooked lower jaw which makes it ugly to look at compared with the symmetry of the spring and summer salmon. But not all the hens are gravid yet, nor all the cock fish looking like kippers. There are still some days left for the fisherman to drink his fill before time is called.

If the best of the fishing is past, so too is the summer heat, when the river is parched and the salmon seek what little current they can find, or die in the stale water. Then only the black-backed gulls prosper.

In comparison with the urgency of spring, when every living thing wants to be on the move, autumn is the time of reflection, on the summer past − and on the winter to come! Of all the four seasons, autumn shows you the true face of the Highlands: the smile on the face of the Sphinx. And what a smile it is, wistful with misty tears and glowing with soft colours. But you know the smile could slip at any moment, and will slip later on in the year, to a scowl of fury. You also know that sublime smile will return, beautiful but always full of guile.

I am getting carried away. This story is about Sally Cartwright and her daughter Jessica.

George Cartwright, Sally's husband, was one of my best friends. I will not say my best friend, because all one's great friends have something special to offer. He first endeared himself to me when, during our National Service, we were on a course together. Anyone who has served in the Army, if only for National Service, knows about courses. You get sent on them for every conceivable area of specialised knowledge from firefighting to sanitation. Somebody has to go on the course. Higher authority says so. You get sent. I have forgotten what course it was that George Cartwright and I were on together, which shows how boring it must have been. Boring to almost everyone except the instructor in charge. At the end of three days of intensive and quite ineffectual brain-washing, our instructor concluded his final lecture: 'Now are there any questions?' 'Yes,' said George. 'What time is the next train to London?'

After we had finished our National Service, George Cartwright went to Cirencester to learn how to make a profit out of farming, which generations of his family had failed to do, and I went up to Cambridge – not so difficult in those days on average brainpower and the right qualifications – with no clear idea of what I wanted to do except enjoy going to parties and meeting new people. As we set out on life from the comfortable haven of college and university, George and I met two or three times a year according to circumstances, either for the weekend at one or another of our houses, or in London. I married first, George left it until very late.

Ann and I were already living at Balmeanie when George Cartwright wrote to ask if he could bring his fiancée up for a few days to stay. Of course, I said, telling him off for not letting me know that he was engaged. A week or two later I met Sally for the first time. Sally was in her early thirties, I guessed, vibrant and attractive rather than classically beautiful. I could not understand why she was still single: girls got married a great deal younger in those days; they did not have careers – or the pill!

We had a riotously happy and funny three days. Sally

laughed her way into our affections, and while she and George were obviously very much in love, they did not bore us by devoting all their attentions to one another. They left plenty over to include Ann and I in their happiness.

Sally was London bred, her knowledge of 'The Country' – to judge from her conversation – was limited to weekend house parties, and the occasional longer visits to relatives in Hampshire and Sussex. I wondered how and where she and George had met. Needless to say she had never seen a salmon except on a fishmonger's slab. George was extremely keen that she should catch one.

When it is important that someone should catch a salmon, I take them to the Falls O' Meanie.

Lunch on the first day of George and Sally's visit was a special one, a lunch to mark an occasion. They had arrived late and tired the night before, and the opportunity to celebrate had been restricted. After a leisurely breakfast, a walk to take in the breathtaking beauty revealed as the mist lifted and hung in wisps to the hills, a chance encounter with Alec Ross in talkative mood, we returned to the Lodge and opened a bottle of champagne. Then we had lunch with another bottle.

After lunch we set off for The Falls o'Meanie. We took just one rod, and mindful of the purpose of the expedition, I suggested George take charge of it.

You fish either the neck or the tail of the pool, depending on how much water there is in the river. At the normal seasonal level the neck offers the better chance. So the neck it was today. To fish here you stand on a pinnacle of rock, we call it the Pulpit, with the full force of the river squeezed into a narrow gorge cascading beside you into the pool beneath, a drop of some fifteen feet or so. The salmon lie beyond the cauldron of bubbles where the current forms again. Depending on the volume of water coming down, it can be a long cast to reach them. George and Sally took up position on the Pulpit, and George began casting. I sat and watched the proceedings on the plank seat which Alec Ross has made for spectators, and ghillies.

As luck would have it after half a dozen casts George hooked a fish.

The hooked salmon behaved predictably, making a long run down the length of the pool, and after a couple of jumps and some weaving around was hauled back to face the force of the current. Unless you are prepared to scramble down a steep rocky face keeping the line taut and free of obstruction, you play your salmon from the Pulpit, whatever the disadvantages of playing a fish from directly above. This much would be evident to any experienced fisherman. And George Cartwright was an experienced fisherman. I guessed he was assessing the chances of Sally landing the salmon if he handed the rod over to her.

I could not hear their conversation, but I saw George take his right hand off the rod, get behind Sally and, putting both arms around her, transfer it to her grasp. Then he stood back leaving her in control. The line slackened for a moment, then Sally reeled up. Off went the fish again making another run down the pool, but this time it did not jump. George was calmness itself. I could not hear his voice raised at all. Fortunate, I thought to myself, that Alec Ross was not in charge of the proceedings.

Luck held and the fish began to tire. There is only one place you can net or gaff a salmon in the Falls O' Meanie pool, and it involves negotiating a dozen or so wooden steps set in the steep bank to the level of the river. This can be a problem if you are on your own, because obviously you have got to keep the strain on, and doing so involves reeling up as you come down the steps; either you watch the fish or you watch the steps, you cannot watch both at the same time. With someone there to net the fish for you there is no very great problem, or should not be. The person with the rod stays on the Pulpit, the person with the net climbs down the steps.

The critical moment of netting Sally's salmon was, barring accidents, fast approaching. I thought to myself, shall I go and do it for them? but discarded the idea on the grounds that the catching of the fish had to be all their own work. Anyway George had the net with him.

I saw George leave Sally's side, walk to the top of the wooden steps down the steep bank, and, net in hand, cautiously descend to the river level. He shouted to her — he had to now — to steer the fish in closer to the bank. I could see the long line from the tip of the rod tight and slanting to meet the water; there was a dangerous splashing and kicking on the surface a yard or so beyond where it did. Another cautionary shout from George, kneeling now, net already half submerged. More kicking and splashing from the fish in protest at being hauled into the shallows. God, I thought, something has got to give in a minute if she keeps up that kind of pressure. George obviously thought so too. I saw him on his knees, one arm supporting his body weight, the other at full stretch, hand grasping what little could be seen above the water of the landing-net handle. The next moment there was an almighty splash and he was in the river.

Although I knew there was little danger of George getting into difficulty where he had fallen in because the water was only a few feet deep, I jumped up to go to his assistance; as I ran towards the steps between where I had been sitting and the Pulpit, I glanced up to see what Sally was doing. She was sitting on the rock with the rod propped up beside her, the line falling slack to the river below, her head bent forward so that I could not see her face, and her shoulders shaking. I thought it must be that initial state of shock which can overtake people in a crisis. I wondered if I should go to her help first. Of George I could see nothing, for the crest of the steep bank hid him from me.

I reached the steps and shouted to Sally. She could not answer. She was in fits of laughter. Looking down to the river I saw a bedraggled George trying to get a foothold on the bank at the same time as holding on to the net with a salmon in it.

Six months after that Sally and George were married, and I was the best man.

George and Sally never had any children of their own; left

88

it a bit late, I suppose. Eventually they adopted a little girl, Jessica she was christened. When she was a bit older she used to come up here with them every year in early September.

If George had hoped that first salmon would hook his future wife on fishing he was disappointed, for she had never really taken to it. She loved fishing, she said, provided the weather was nice and she was left to get on with it in her own way: either with a good book, or with a pencil and sketch-pad. This was in no sense meant to be a disparaging remark. They each got a great deal of pleasure out of going to the places where George fished, and Sally either read or sketched or wandered off on her own. And afterwards, when they came to talk about how they had spent the day, each had a different story to tell.

Then two years ago George Cartwright suddenly had a heart attack. Within twenty-four hours he was dead. He was in his late fifties, Sally five years or so younger, and Jessica fourteen.

I never was much good at keeping a stiff upper lip. At George's memorial service they sang the hymn 'All Things Bright and Beautiful'. I got as far as:

'The purple-headed mountain,
The river running by,
The sunset, and the morning,
That brightens up the sky.'

Then my voice choked and I could no longer read the blurred words on the service sheet.

That was in April. At the beginning of August, I had a letter from Sally Cartwright asking if she and Jessica could come up and stay as usual. Ann and I were gratified that Sally should want to come, but a little concerned about one of her likely reasons for doing so. Could it be to recapture a little bit of her life with George, which simply would not be here without him? We thought of ways and means of softening the impact. We decided to have them on our own to begin with, then we told Ernest Cantrell what the situation was, and invited him up for a week, the first few days to coincide with the last of Sally and Jessica's stay.

Sally and Jessica duly came at the beginning of September. Of course, the spirit of George was there in the background, but except for a few quiet moments Sally seemed to draw comfort from being at Balmeanie. It is that sort of place. Ernest Cantrell played his part perfectly. He had, after all, a good deal of background experience. Jessica and he got on like a house on fire.

A year later, early September, and Sally and Jessica came again to stay. Ann drove in to Inverness to collect them. We had invited Ernest Cantrell too, but earlier in the week of their stay. He readily accepted.

At breakfast the day after she and Jessica had arrived, Sally said, 'I never really did get interested in catching fish. Perhaps it was a good thing after all. I don't think there would have been room for two of us in George's private world by the riverside. I showed willing to begin with, but I think he was quite relieved when I didn't take him on at his own game. What is this bug that gets into people and makes them want to catch fish?'

'Oh anyone can get it, young or old,' I said. 'It attacked me when I was quite young, George too, I think. Ernie Cantrell caught it when he was much older. Once fishing gets into the system, you might as well accept that people who are immune to it will always think you mad.'

'Women must be particularly resistant, then,' Ann joined in. 'I'm like Sally, I've lived with a fisherman for nearly twenty years, the river's a few hundred yards away, and I'm not mad about fishing. What about you Jessica, do you think you'll ever catch the bug? Our children haven't.'

Jessica looked thoughtful. 'I don't know,' she replied, 'I always remember one of Dad's favourite sayings. Someone called Izaak Walton wrote it in the seventeenth century, he told me. "All that are lovers of virtue, and dare trust in His providence, and be quiet, and go a-angling." I could find out for myself, couldn't I?'

'You could indeed,' I said. I got to thinking how and when the fishing bug had first caught me.

When I was a boy I lived in a part of England where the fishing was limited to coarse fish. It was long before the days of the 'put-and-take' trout lakes. There was a river within easy bicycling distance, small and sluggish, idling its way through fields of rank grass past a place which was known locally as the Stanch: a brick bridge carrying a path over the river, a spillway beneath, and on the downstream side of the bridge, a deeper pool of quite clear water. The village kids came to swim in the Stanch, and it was this attraction which first brought me there. When the bathers had gone, shoals of small fish returned to forage.

The local lads with their single-cane rods, small centre-pin reels, worms, maggots and dough, came here. It hardly occurred to me then to question why they came to fish. Now that I did so, the only answer that I could find was that some instinct had drawn generations of lads to come and catch fish at the Stanch, which if they asked their mothers to cook for them, pride alone would force them to eat. So if I first came to the Stanch to bathe there, why did I watch the fish, and want to catch them? For exactly the same reason as the village lads: instinct, natural instinct.

The fishing bug lay dormant in me for years when opportunity was lacking, and there were other more urgent things to get on with, like growing up. Then my job took me to Ulster, to South Armagh, bandit territory now but not then; a lush countryside of bog, rush, and hilly green fields rising to steep heather-covered moorland, through which flowed rivers feeding into Lough Neagh – the largest natural freshwater lake in the United Kingdom. I lived in a small flat above the stables of a big country house. In the long summer evenings I was bored; I wanted something to occupy my time, and my interest. I turned again to the rivers, and to the lakes – loughs in Ireland – as if directed by instinct to investigate.

How I first came to Benburb on the River Blackwater I cannot remember. I must have heard the locals say that there

91

were salmon in the river, and fishing for them was mostly free. This would have been enough to make me prick up my ears and use my tongue to find out more. The readiness of the average Ulsterman to pass on helpful information, especially on matters like fishing, would have done the rest. I went to Benburb to investigate.

As I watched a salmon going up the fish pass, I knew that I had to come back here with a rod and line.

There was a weir at Benburb, and an industrial building of some sort, presumably a disused mill; a natural fault in the river's course had evidently been exploited to harness the flow of water for some purpose, but so far as I can remember there was no mill race. There was, however, a big pool, the only one to be seen either upstream or down, and salmon congregated here before going over the weir upstream. This was the only attractive feature of the place.

To the fisherman, novice or veteran, seeing fish is believing you can catch them. I saw the salmon at Benburb. One day I would catch a salmon, and I would catch it on a fly the way I had read salmon ought to be caught. I had faith, but no rod, no reel, no line, no flies, and no experience.

The problem of the rod was solved by acquiring one from an elderly uncle; it was discovered in an attic, it was made of greenheart, the rings swivelled where they were whipped on, it was fourteen feet long when the three sections were put together, and it was extremely heavy. There was no reel to go with the rod so I bought an aluminium one, together with line of some sort. From the same source as this rod I had another bonus; a leather wallet (which I still have, and use) with interleaved parchment pages sewn into compartments, and felt pads. Hooked into the felt pads was an assortment of salmon flies, most of them with yellowing gut eyes; these I reluctantly discarded as being well past use-by date. Ever optimistic, I bought myself a gaff hook and bound it with twine to a long wooden handle.

A salmon river which offers free fishing attracts more fishermen than it does fish; this I soon discovered after I began to come regularly once or twice a week to Benburb. Most days after work the place had its quota of anglers poised like herons where they had staked their claim to fish, spinning and worming, the occasional one casting a fly. Salmon which reached that pool, travelling up the River Bann, through Lough Neagh, and into the Blackwater to Benburb, in all fifty miles from the sea, were not easy to deceive; the odd one or two were fooled — and landed — but not many. What the local anglers thought of me with my great pole of a rod, casting and casting my fly until I was too tired and fed up to continue, I have no idea. But I watched them, listened to their conversation, and when I got to know a few asked them for their advice which, being natural fishermen, they readily gave.

The fishing bug had infected me, but I could still have been cured. The remedy I now know lies in making yourself believe that you will never catch anything. I came near to believing that. It depends on your resistance. If at the end of a day spent flogging a river, despite weary limbs, tired eyes, biting midges or bitter cold, and an increasing sense of hopelessness gained from seeing fish you cannot catch or, worse, not seeing any fish at all, you want to come back for more, you are infected. If after many such days, weeks, months even, you still want to come back for more, you are badly infected. This incubation period is critical; it usually ends either in complete rejection or catching your first fish. The time obviously varies with the conditions. In my case it ended in addiction after six months.

I would not for choice go to fish where others go; being alone by the river is more important to me than waiting my turn down the pool. At Benburb I came to know when to expect a casting of anglers: the weekends, of course, and early-closing day; the first part of the week was the best time to come. Seldom was the place empty. I preferred to wander from where the others were whipping away at the water, hoping that in a less favoured place one day some solitary salmon would share my fly. The farther side of the river was not so easily accessible, and, together with the fact that fish were not seen to be caught from this bank, this meant that you had the place more to yourself. I usually went there.

I had come to Benburb regularly since the spring, and the season on the Blackwater was due to end in three weeks time. I could now cast well enough with my unwieldy equipment. God knows I'd had enough practice. On the advice of some of the locals, I had added considerably to my inherited collection of salmon flies, following their conviction that the only possible fly to use was a Fiery Brown, a Hairy Mary, and a dozen more besides. With the other anglers, I had watched in envy as one of our number actually hooked and landed a salmon. I had cast much myself but caught nothing, not even had the comforting thought that a fish had actually come to look at my fly before turning away from it in rejection.

One day I was in my favourite position on the far bank. I had cast my fly for the umpteenth time into the deep streamy water, and as it came round deep down under the steep bank, it was grabbed.

Then for the first time I felt the solid weight of a salmon. It was not a very lively salmon, it did not jump or rush all around the pool, but without any doubt there was a salmon on the end of my line. All I wanted was to land it safely.

I did land the salmon. It was not a beautiful clean-run fish, but brown and not very big. Neither did it taste too good, but oh, the pride in eating a fish you have caught yourself, whatever it tastes like.

Walking back towards the Lodge I wondered what would have happened if I had never hooked that salmon, let alone landed it. Would the period of quarantine have ended in my rejection of the fishing bug altogether? I think not: it had been lurking in me since those days at the Stanch, and even if I had not come to live at Balmeanie, I would have been struck down elsewhere. Then why had my own son and daughter not been infected? They had lived in a far more contagious environment than I.

The following day Ernest Cantrell joined us. Except for a

thank-you letter, I had not heard from him since he last came to stay in June. I was not about when he arrived after tea, but Ann told me later that Sally Cartwright had greeted him like an old friend. It was easy enough to do that with Ernest, but later that evening when Jessica, too, was sitting on the sofa with him chatting away, I did begin to wonder whether it had been a full year since the three of them last met.

Later on that week I had to go to Inverness for the day. When I got back, about half an hour before dinner, I went into the study where the Cartwrights and Ernest Cantrell were sitting having a drink – Ann was presumably supervising dinner. I could sense that something had happened. There was one of those pregnant silences which usually mean that two people are bursting to tell you the same thing, but do not want to say it together.

Ernest said it first. 'Jessica and I have been fishing today, up at Lochan Na'Keel,' he began.

'I didn't think you knew the place,' I interrupted, 'it's full of small trout – we tried to net some of them out to give the others more feeding and a chance to grow a bit bigger. I've never caught anything there over a quarter of a pound.'

'We did. Shall we tell him now or later, Jessica?'

'I can't bear to tell him,' she said. 'You tell him later.'

Sally was not standing for this conversational dalliance. She got up. 'I know what happened. I was there, remember? I'm not going to listen to another blow-by-blow account. I'm going out to see if I can help Ann,' she said. So Ernest told me what did happen later.

If you take the track up the strath, following the course of the Balmeanie Burn for three miles or so, you come to a square of stunted firs stuck on the hillside like a stamp on a blank envelope. You cannot penetrate that wood; it is a tangle of twisted branches, the home base for marauding foxes intent on plundering lambs. Wildcats live there, too, they say, but I have never seen one. We tried to burn the place down, but it would not burn. Then you come to a derelict lodge. Only the lower storey remains standing, and the empty spaces where the front windows used to be look forlornly out over Lochan Na'Keel.

I imagine that when the lodge had its resident host, hostess, and their guests, on the warm summer evenings Lochan Na'Keel provided them with after-dinner fishing. But now there is no one (except me) to take a personal interest in the loch, there are too many trout after too little feeding. I seldom go there. To tell the truth I find the place rather depressing, the ruined lodge a sad reminder of the happy people, at least I think of them as happy, who once lived there. Now only the jagged remains of what they built stand starkly staring out over the loch to watch me jealously. Maybe they left a jinx when they finally departed and handed Lochan Na'Keel back to the wild: I have never caught a trout over six inches long there. I do not tell people about the loch as a place worth fishing. Ernest must have discovered it for himself in his wanderings up the Balmeanie Burn.

'I don't suppose you appreciated it in Inverness, but it was the most perfect morning,' began Ernest. 'I suggested to Sally and Jessica that we should go on Ernie's Mystery Mountain Tour and take a picnic lunch with us. I had in mind a trip to Lochan Na'Keel. I thought the ruined lodge beside the lochan would appeal to Sally's artistic temperament, besides which it was unlikely that her husband had ever bothered to fish there, so the place would hold no sad memories for her. Ann said we could take the Land-Rover. I slipped my trout rod in the back with our picnic gear.

'When we got up to Lochan Na'Keel, Sally wandered off with her sketch book. Jessica and I set about baling out that terrible old boat of yours, and it took us the best part of half an hour before we managed to get it on its side and empty out the rest of the water. Jessica said she'd row while I fished; she wasn't bad at it either. For an hour or so we cruised around the loch, and I caught several small trout, which I couldn't bring myself to knock on the head. By then I thought Jessica needed a rest from her rowing. I suggested this to her, and after protesting she wasn't a bit tired, she pulled into the bank and we changed over.

'Once we were clear of the shallows, I let go of the oars and, picking up the rod, cast, then began rowing once more, stripping the reel between each pull, until the line sank in the water a couple of boat-lengths astern. I handed the rod to Jessica in the stern and rowed slowly around the loch. We hadn't been trolling for long before I saw the rod-tip kick and kick again as a small trout was dragged along in our wake. I told Jessica to reel up and swing the little fish inboard, and it landed wriggling in the bottom of the boat. "Wet your hand before picking it up," I told her. She worked the fly free. Don't throw the fish, I said, when you put it back, or you may injure it. She leant over the thwart and released the trout. Then she smiled at me. "Do you have anything in a larger size?" she said.

'That remark gave me an idea.

'It wasn't long before we caught another fingerling trout. This time, instead of putting the fish back, I knocked it on the head. I changed the cast for a stronger length of nylon, at the end of which I tied a triangle hook, then passing the nylon through the fish's gills, I hooked the triangle in its side. I completed the process by pinching a rusty bottle-top which I found in the bottom of the boat to the line end of the cast to act as a sinker. We were in business for serious trolling. Where there are lots of small trout there could also be a large one eating them, I reasoned.

'To cut a long story short, I had been rowing around for half an hour or so when it happened: a yelp from Jessica, line ripped off the reel — fortunately she didn't try to check it — and a grab by me for the rod. After that first explosion of activity I got a bit more organised. The trout was big. I'd seen that and felt his weight, but with a strong cast in an open loch there should be no great problem in dealing with him. I toyed with the idea of handing the rod back to Jessica, but thought better of it. What was the point in risking the loss of such a grand trout, and possibly her confidence as well? Perhaps later, I thought, when I've taken some of the steam out of him.

'I won't bore you with the details of the tussle, even though there were some nasty moments. After about ten minutes I got the fish alongside the boat, well up in the water, and more or less done for. As I thought! I guessed he must be between three and four pounds in weight. Now was the time to hand the rod to Jessica while I netted him. I did so, telling her to hold him steady, and keep the line taut.

'I slipped the landing-net into the water behind the fish, but he must have seen me, or perhaps the rim of the net touched his tail. Did I say barring accidents? The done-for trout reacted violently to whatever I'd done to make him aware of his imminent peril. He shot forward. I did an Alec Ross and yelled at Jessica to give him some line. Of course she had no idea what I meant. I saw the curve of the rod, and I saw Jessica's right hand firm on the button of the reel, keeping the line taut as I'd told her. Then following my latest instruction she wound the reel — anti-clockwise. A moment later the rod was straight again.

'Jessica looked at me. She didn't have to say anything, we both felt the same. I suggested we went ashore and had our picnic.'

That, so far as I can remember the telling of it, was Ernest's account of the morning's excursion-turned-drama. I have listened to a great many people telling me how they caught this fish or lost that one. There is seldom a third party involved, except perhaps a ghillie, in the supporting role. Ernest Cantrell himself had been guilty of talking up his fishing exploits, beginning with how he had battled with his first salmon, and Alec Ross. Now there was less of 'I', more of 'we', to his account. I was beginning to guess why. Apart from that, I was grateful to him for the evidence that at least there was one big trout in Lochan Na'Keel.

The rest of the week passed uneventfully, except for the fact that Ernest seemed to spend less of his time fishing on his own, and more in the company of Sally and Jessica.

On Saturday morning, the last day of Ernest's and the two Cartwright's stay, a small package came by registered post addressed to Jessica. Alan the postie arrives in his red Royal Mail Land-Rover any time between ten and twelve in the morning. Nobody was about when he came, so I signed for the parcel, and put it on the hall table.

They were all back at lunchtime, and I fetched the package for Jessica. She took it in her hand, turning the small neat parcel over, examining the writing, before picking at the sellotape with her finger-nails. Her obvious curiosity had worked on the rest of us, and we gathered round as she removed the brown wrapping paper. Inside was a red morocco jewel case. Jessica pressed the little gold button and the case sprung open, revealing a silver bracelet. She took it out, and the bracelet dangled from her fingers as she held it up. There was obviously an inscription, which she was reading. Then she handed it to her mother, and, without a word, made for Ernest and planted a smacking kiss on his cheek.

Sally passed the bracelet round for the rest of us to look at. When it came to my turn I saw that on the chain was a silver fish, scales jointed together to make it look as if it could swim. Next to the clasp was a narrow segment of silver on which was engraved, 'In place of the one that got away'.

Alec Ross has a sixth sense which alerts him to the time at which our guests are departing. He has come to terms with the fact that they often travel south on a Sunday. At first, when I saw him hanging around in the yard at half-past nine on a Sunday morning, I thought someone had forgotten to tip him. Later I came to the conclusion that he considered this interruption of his Sunday was worthwhile in order to establish future goodwill.

Alec's farewell varied according to his grading of our guests. With Ernest Cantrell there existed between them the brotherhood of the National Union of Railwaymen which had deposited them at their different stations in life.

On the Sunday of that week when the two Cartwrights and Ernest Cantrell were due to depart, Alec Ross was hovering off-stage, waiting for the cue to make his entry. His sense of timing is usually good. Sure enough, when Ann had done her round of kisses, Alec strode on stage, the gravel sweep in front of the lodge. He shook hands all round. 'Gang warily, Sir Ernest,' he said, 'forbye we want to see you and her leddyship back agin next year.' Then realising his slip, he coloured bright red. It was the first time that I had seen Alec Ross forget the rest of his lines.

# Chapter Ten

# It Takes All Sorts...

'But now the sport is marde, and wott ye why?
Fishes decrease, and fishers multiply.'
                                        (Thomas Bastard, 1598)

As I get older the prospect of the winter becomes more
forbidding each year. November comes: no sunshine, no
warmth in the air, no sign of the animals and birds of summer,
no fishing, no one staying. And five months of it to come.
Waiting for the spring becomes an obsession. We do escape
for a little. But Balmeanie is our home.

March can open the door with a glimpse of a world free of
mist, rain, ice, or snow; but it is slammed in our faces almost
immediately. I remember one such day last year, when the
door was open and a weak sun shone. I decided to go and look
at the sheep, getting what nourishment they could from the
grass by the river. I walked along the Struie, running high
from melting snow, crossed the plank bridge where the
Balmeanie Burn joins the main river, climbed the steep brae
on the other side, and looked down on the necklace of pools
to the bend which is our boundary. There on the far bank
was someone fishing the topmost pool of the Callan Beat.

The fishing on the Callan Beat belongs to the Glentore
Estate and is let on timeshare, described by the agents as an
'exciting leisure development'.

From early April until the beginning of June the beat is as
good as any on the Struie. Before that the salmon are backed
up down the river waiting for warmth and water to get over

the Morie Falls a mile downstream; the odd one may make it earlier to Callan, but not many. I wondered what the tenant was paying for his share of the exciting leisure.

The thought struck me that I could let my fishing very profitably, both to me and to the timeshare agency. But how could I bring myself to meet people like that man down there whose money I would be taking, talk to them as one fisherman to another, knowing what their chances were of catching a salmon at this time of year? Like a secondhand car-dealer, the agent meets the punters only once. I would have to meet them every year.

For the umpteenth time I was trying to hang my kind of fishing on other people, like choosing their pictures or furniture for them. You cannot do it, any more than you can persuade someone who likes them that china ducks on a wall do not look beautiful. Maybe that fisherman knew what his chances were, had taken the trouble to find out how many salmon were caught at this time of year on the Callan Beat, and still thought it worth his while to have the sole ownership of a stretch of salmon river for the same time each year. Mine, all mine for a fortnight, or a month.

I had read in an article on timeshare that the formula for rentals was 'the per fish value'. How much a 'unit of salmon fishing' (sic) was worth was based on historic catches. This method of valuation, in the writer's opinion, had been taken too literally as, and I quote, 'a standard of sporting satisfaction and fulfilment'. According to the same article you can now have a choice, and select your 'holiday opportunity' from a 'menu' which includes skiing, golf, riding, and salmon fishing.

I wondered how the object of my present curiosity, the fisherman I was watching, squared his sporting satisfaction and fulfilment with the per fish value he was paying on the Callan Beat at this time of year. Or perhaps he had selected salmon fishing from the menu. I turned and went to look at my sheep. As I was walking home I reflected on the new breed of salmon fisherperson. My own experience had been limited to our guests, most of whom had grown up with fishing, or like Ernest Cantrell stumbled on it later in life to find peace and enchantment. I cannot claim to know the *nouveaux riches* of the salmon rivers. What I do know is that if I had no fishing of my own, I would not buy it like a new car with the current year's registration mark.

I do not want my fishing organised for me, casting a fly down a well-manicured beat with a ghillie in attendance, even if it does mean catching more fish. I like wild fishing and I like lonely fishing. Time enough for the chat later. Am I an eccentric? I think not. Ernest Cantrell understands my kind of fishing, and I understand his. I am an old hand, he is a novice, but we both value most our freedom to fish as we want.

I much prefer catching a salmon on the fly, preferably a small fly fished on a floating line near the surface. You see everything happening, which is the greatest thrill of all. But when conditions are hopeless for any kind of fly what is the fisherman expected to do — pack up and go home? The answer, quite often, is yes. I know of a beat where fly only is the rule. One particularly poor season when the fishing tenants could not reach the usual number of units of salmon based on historic catches, the owner, Lord Tomnoddy (which is not his real name), took over. In an effort to achieve an acceptable per fish value, he spun, wormed, and prawned. All perfectly legal elsewhere on the river, but banned to his tenants.

Another river demands that only a husband and wife may fish the same beat. Heaven knows why! Other leasors stipulate that you must have a ghillie in attendance, presumably to pay the man's wages and see that you do not cheat.

The inheritors chasing the earners, old money trying to grab a slice of new money. Both seem to me to be getting it a bit wrong.

I remembered staying near Aviemore and walking down to the Spey. I was not fishing. I came across a young lad carrying an eight-foot rod with a fixed spool reel on it, and a gleaming fresh-run salmon which I guessed must be ten pounds or so in weight. I congratulated him on his catch and asked him what he was going to do with the fish. He looked at me witheringly. 'Flog it to one of the local hotels, of course,' he said. I suppose he had paid a few quid to the local fishing association for his permit, and stood to get fifteen or twenty from the hotel for his salmon. How's that for per fish value?

I suppose I could have made the effort to talk to the fisherman I had seen that morning, but had I done so it would only have been to pass the time of day. I could hardly ask him if he considered he was getting sporting satisfaction and fulfilment from his timeshare investment. Neither am I likely to ask anyone else I meet with a rod in their hands why they come fishing. Like most of us, my impressions are based on what I read and what I hear. Over the years that we have been taking paying guests at Balmeanie, I have come to learn that you cannot expect people who pay for their fishing to conform to your credo. Many do, some do not.

I hope I am not priggish, but I do not respond to the call for instant friendship implicit in being addressed by my Christian name on first introduction. I also shy away from being made the recipient of unsolicited confidences by relative strangers. Within six hours of meeting Mr Raymond Snaith I had encountered both experiences. First impressions are dangerous, I know, but at the end of the same period of time I also guessed that I was paying the price for the breakdown of our system for selecting guests. There was another reason, too, for my rueful mood, and I will come to that later.

Until his letter arrived, Mr Snaith was an unknown quantity to us. He wrote asking if we could have him for a week (it is usually a minimum of a fortnight, so that we get to know people) at a time when we had very few bookings. We, I, made the mistake of failing to follow our vetting procedure — finding a character witness before having anyone we do not know to stay. In his letter, headed Raymond Snaith Investments and giving a West End of London address, Mr

Snaith said that the Glentore Estate Office had recommended Balmeanie to him as a lodge which took paying guests for the fishing; his company occasionally needed to entertain important clients, he would like to come and see what we had to offer. Greed overcame caution, and I wrote to say I would be pleased to have him.

I like to be present when guests arrive. I think of our paying guests as friends coming to stay, which in nine cases out of ten they are. On the Sunday evening when Mr Snaith was due to arrive, I was down by the river trimming back some bushes which sooner or later were going to attract someone's fly, when I saw a bronze-coloured Range Rover cross the bridge. I began walking back to the house.

As I skirted the out-buildings and came round to the gravel sweep in front of the lodge, a big black labrador bounded up and sniffed suspiciously at my trouser leg then, deciding that I was nice to know, tried to jump up in greeting. I repulsed the dog, and walked over to where a man was getting his luggage out of the back of the Range Rover. Hearing my footsteps on the gravel, Mr Snaith straightened up and asked if my name was Charles Rowley. I said that it was, and he introduced himself, adding as he pointed in the dog's direction, 'Hope you don't mind Nigger, he always comes with me when I go fishing.'

We have come across the dog problem before, people asking do we mind if they bring one, even two. After a few tactful enquiries on the telephone about the animal's size, sex, behaviour pattern, and sleeping habits, we can usually resolve the situation one way or another, and the dog comes or is left behind, according to my assessment of its nuisance factor.

This may involve a certain amount of duplicity on my part (our bitches spend a long time on heat!) if I decide against risking the disruption of the household by having some vast quadruped sleeping upstairs, but on the whole we have managed to avoid hurt feelings.

I was the one with hurt feelings now, but I decided to be conciliatory. I could hardly be otherwise, without telling Mr

Snaith to turn round and go home. As I opened the front door for us to go inside, carrying Mr Snaith's suitcase in the other hand, Nigger shouldered past, nearly knocking me off balance. I heard an angry shout from Ann, and guessed that he had made her acquaintance.

That evening Mr Snaith told us all about his business, his home, his previous fishing experience, and his wife – who at one time had been his secretary. Nigger, after he had deposited a massive turd on the gravel outside the front door, was quartered in the boot room.

On Monday morning I went with Snaith to introduce him to Alec Ross. Nigger accompanied us. Alec did not appreciate the 'Good morning ghillie' he got when the introduction was effected. 'Ma name's Alec Ross, I'm no a waiter,' he said tersely. I thought I had better leave them to it.

An hour or so before lunch, my conscience nagged at me for leaving Alec and Mr Snaith to establish a working relationship on their own. I thought I had better go and see how they were getting on. I need not have worried, for after the initial friction at their meeting, all the signs were that harmony had been restored. I could see Raymond Snaith fishing down the pool to the accompaniment of Alec Ross's commentary.

Nigger was sitting bolt upright on a vantage point which he had selected on the river bank, alert and watching like a sentry on duty. A salmon jumped at the tail of the pool. The dog began to move his tail very deliberately from side to side, and the flaps of his ears stood out on his head; even from behind I could guess at his thoughts. Nigger's natural instincts were aroused. But with commendable restraint he remained at his post.

Obviously all was well with Raymond Snaith, with Alec, and with Nigger. I left them to the enjoyment of their fishing.

Snaith was not an objectionable man, indeed he did his best to be friendly, but in an overstated way. He assumed we would be interested in him and his friends, his achievements and his ambitions. Any attempt to deflect him was listened to but not heard. You could see it in his eyes. They were not connecting with yours but fixed somewhere in the middle distance, while he concentrated on what he was going to tell you once you had finished speaking. Dinner-table conversation, or for that matter any other conversation, was an uphill struggle. We tried a wide variety of leads, but soon found out that general discussion was not Mr Snaith's strong point. Either he expressed the definitive view, or else we passed on to the next item on the agenda proposed by Ann or myself. The only prompts which got him going were those which could be used to tell us more about himself. And yet if there was a real Raymond Snaith, neither Ann nor I could discover him.

I am not especially interested in how an investment company works, but by the middle of that week I had perforce learned a great deal. It was all a matter of confidence, I was told, building up confidence with potential investors, getting to know them, wining and dining them, playing golf with them, knowing the face that controls the money supply. It was amazing, Snaith said, what business you could bring in over a round of golf. For what reason did he come fishing, I wondered: to relax from his business affairs, or to extend them?

At least there was nothing complicated about Nigger. Here at Balmeanie he was back to basics, the basics of his breeding. Freedom at last, freedom to follow the instincts suppressed since puppyhood. Nose to the ground he explored the byways through the heather and bracken. Rabbits, he discovered to his annoyance, lived down holes, and squirrels up trees. One evening when he was let out before going to bed, he returned ten minutes later, wagging his tail and bearing in his blood-spattered mouth a hedgehog, which he dumped in triumph on the hall floor. Nigger had found his true vocation. He was a sporting dog. But I am not sure that I would have cared to take him out shooting with me.

As for Alec Ross, after his initial tiff with Mr Snaith he had seen the light, and seen it in the shape of the expensive bronze-coloured Range Rover now parked in the garage. Both men had a professional interest in weighing up the potential of their clients. Shrewd ghillie that he was, Alec would realise that the potential of his client would only be fully realised if he caught a salmon. He would also have noticed that Mr Snaith's knowledge of fishing was limited to being able to cast a fly, and whatever he might say to the contrary, any salmon he caught was likely to be his first. That could prove an added bonus when it came to the matter of tipping. By the end of Wednesday not a salmon had been caught.

Raymond Snaith could hardly complain about the lack of fish. They were plainly there for him to see, if not to catch. On Wednesday evening, I made the mistake of asking him how he had got on. He said he had not touched a thing all day, adding bleakly that he thought the fish in the river were very stale. He managed to imply that he could hardly be expected to catch stale fish. How, I wondered, did he come to know how long the salmon had been in our part of the river? I detected Alec laying off the odds in case of failure to catch one by the end of the week. I thought I had better take a hand in things myself.

On Thursday morning I went with Raymond Snaith, Alec, and Nigger to the head of Balmeanie Pool, a grand holding pool in the classic manner of a Highland river. Unlike the Falls O' Meanie, here there is no step in the river bed. The flow of water is constricted by the rock on either bank, and century by century it has forced its way through. Now there is a channel of bubbling water flowing evenly over the course which it has carved, until being finally released into the depths of the long wide pool it has had such trouble in reaching.

From a salmon's point of view, this is the perfect place to rest. There is oxygen. There are lying places behind the stones in the neck. Streamy water flows between the undercut rock on either bank, and the pool has a wide tail to play about in as the night approaches.

I did not think for a moment that my presence would improve Raymond Snaith's chances of catching a fish, but I thought it would be diplomatic to show a personal interest in his doing so. He began fishing at the head of the pool, Alec took up his stance level with him on the bank, and I kept in the background. Nigger gave up his investigation of the rabbit potential that morning, and took post on a springy patch of turf beside the path where he could watch the proceedings.

Even the most experienced fisherman knows that without an element of luck on his side his skills and knowledge alone will not necessarily land him a salmon. Conversely, the inexperienced fisherman with luck on his side can throw any fly he likes and catch fish. It happened that morning. Luck came to Raymond Snaith. After about half an hour of casting down the pool he was into a fish. Alec's voice took on the urgency of a racing commentary five furlongs from home, but Snaith got the gist of it, and a measure of control over the salmon. He had a dangerous amount of line out, and like most novices was not putting on enough strain. I could see only a slight curve in the rod. But time and the drag of the line told. After about ten minutes the runs became shorter, and the fish rolled on the surface before boring down once more. It looked as if Raymond Snaith was on the way to catching his first salmon.

Watching someone else playing a salmon depends for its dramatic quality on who the fisher is and what the salmon does. On this occasion if there had been little drama, there was a good deal of relief on my part as I watched Alec Ross get ready with his net. During the fifteen minutes or so it had taken to play the fish, I had remained where I was, not wishing to intrude on the two principals. Then came the drama. Nigger made his entry.

I watched spellbound as the dog raced along the bank. Then, four legs in the air, like a dressage horse doing the capriole, he took off into the river, landing in the water in front of Alec. The latter let out a yell, and raising his free arm to wipe his dripping face, cursed the dog, shock mingling with outrage. Nigger heeded him not, nor the shouts of his master. He had a duty to do, to retrieve that strange creature in the water. Puzzled that he had not landed on his quarry, Nigger swam out into midstream and, treading water, looked for its whereabouts. The tired salmon must have been galvanised into renewed activity by the sudden appearance of a huge spreadeagled creature against the sky above. I heard the rip of the reel, and realised that the cast had somehow remained unbroken. I also realised that if the fish came to the surface Nigger would be on to it like a flash, while if it remained submerged he might not realise that his master's line was attached to it. Now was the time for me to play my part.

Oblivious to the shouts from the bank, Nigger continued to swim about vigorously, knowing there was something in this unfamiliar element which had to be retrieved but, deprived of scent, having to rely on sight. And reading the dog's mind this way, I saw my chance. I must keep him occupied while the other two landed the salmon.

If I threw a stick, the dog might swim ashore at the very point where the disgruntled Alec was having a second go at netting the salmon. I feared for the consequences to Nigger. Stones first, a stick later, I thought to myself. I shouted my plan to the other two. It was received without enthusiasm by Alec, who gabbled something about wishing he had brought 'his bluidy gaff wi' him'. Snaith was busy trying to subdue the fish. I picked up a stone and threw it to land a couple of yards behind Nigger. He heard the splash, turned, saw the ripples, and went to investigate. I threw another stone, this time twenty yards downstream towards the far bank. The dog swam off again vigorously in that direction. But Nigger was no fool, and would soon realise that there was no connection between these rings he was seeing in the water and the plunging, splashing creature he was looking for. I had to hope that a floating stick would confuse him.

I saw the line from Raymond Snaith's rod entering the water at a sharp downward angle a few yards out from the bank, and Alec waiting ready with the net. Whatever he might have to say later, and I guessed it would be plenty,

Alec Ross was not one to let a salmon go by default. Now was the time to throw the stick to divert Nigger. But could I find a stick? Twigs, yes, a dead branch six foot long, a waterlogged plank, but nothing which I could throw any distance that would float. And meanwhile Nigger was swimming around looking for clues. Desperately I searched my mind for a contingency plan. I had it. 'Nigger,' I yelled, 'rabbits!' And I waved my cap in the air. The dog turned his head towards me, and I ran down to the river and began splashing in the water. I had his attention now, he swam in my direction. I dropped my cap in. 'Fetch it Nigger, fetch it,' I urged, pointing to the floating cap. Nose outstretched, eyes fixed, the dog struck out powerfully in pursuit. I had fooled him.

I had been so involved with putting my deception plan into effect that I had not noticed how they were getting on with the salmon. Now I heard a splash from behind me, heard Alec's exhortation to 'Hold the damn fush steady.' Nigger heard the splash, too. He did a U-turn, and began paddling flat out upstream. My cap floated away.

Nigger was just too late; by the time he arrived the salmon was already on the bank, dead. He licked it from head to tail. Then he shook the water off his coat, all over Alec who had just taken the fish out of the landing-net.

In our game book the entry for that day in the Remarks column reads, 'Nigger's fish'.

Mr Snaith left at the end of the week. He thanked us and drove away with Nigger in his bronze-coloured Range Rover. He did not write. I wondered whether he had enjoyed himself; it was difficult to tell with people like Raymond Snaith. If it had not been for Nigger, I think I would have forgotten about him by now.

A much less forgettable person, both as a guest and as a fisherman, was Jim Morrison. So too was his wife. He came to us out of the blue on the recommendation of Tim Wedderburn, one of our regular visitors. Apart from saying he thought we would get on well with Jim Morrison, Tim did not tell us much more about him. Morrison himself telephoned a week or so later and we fixed a date for him to come, with his wife.

I was not about when the Morrisons arrived, some minor crisis to sort out with the sheep had taken me up the hill. I met them when I got back at teatime. He was a man somewhere in his late fifties or early sixties, tall, with a long, angular, clean-shaven face, and faraway eyes which rekindled with interest when they met yours; he was wearing a tweed coat and grey flannel trousers. She was a good deal younger, in her forties I would think, slim and elegant in maroon-coloured slacks and fawn cashmere jersey. Morrison introduced her to me as Phyllida. She looked at me with the assurance of an attractive woman, and held out her hand for me to take. I did so, and she let it remain for a few moments as her eyes kept their hold on mine, then she withdrew her hand and her glance shifted to take in Ann as well. 'What a beautiful place this is,' she said, 'I know Jim and I are going to be happy here.'

We found plenty to talk about over dinner that evening, but comparing notes when we went to bed, neither Ann nor I had been able to discover what Jim Morrison did for a living, where exactly they lived, what children they had; anything, in fact, about their personal lives. Nor had either of us been able to probe successfully for any mutual friends, other than the Wedderburns. Morrison listened with obvious interest to what anyone else was saying before he replied, and when he did so it was to invite further comment before he expressed his own opinion. Even then I got the impression that he held himself in check, his natural modesty failing to conceal entirely that he knew a good deal more than he thought it appropriate to reveal. She too was an easy partner in conversation; making the running or responding to someone else's cue, light-hearted or serious in the manner she judged fitted the mood of the moment. It struck me that they would be good companions for the next fourteen days.

The next morning at breakfast, Jim Morrison asked would I mind if they had a ghillie for a couple of days, then fished

112

on their own. Not at all, I said. In fact that morning Alec Ross had asked for the day off to go to a funeral, so I took the Morrisons myself. There were plenty of salmon up, but they had been there for some time now, and the river was low. I thought we would start on the first pool down from the Falls O'Meanie, and fish on downstream. Then, if there was nothing doing, we could try the Falls in the evening, their best chance of a salmon. Neither of the Morrisons had given me a clue as to how experienced they were. I soon guessed from the look of their gear and the way they put it together that neither of them was new to the sport. Jim Morrison handed me a worn pocket-sized aluminium fly-box and asked what flies I would suggest they used. I selected a small Blue Charm, and a slightly larger Thunder and Lightning, both tied on low-water hooks. I asked if they wanted me to take one of them on to the next pool – there was only stream enough for one rod to fish at a time – but Jim Morrison said he would watch while Phyllida fished, then he would have a go.

We worked our way down from pool to pool, seeing the long grey shapes of salmon lying on the bottom tucked in against the rock where they could get some shade from the climbing sun, the only sign of life the occasional glimpse of white from a languidly opening mouth. Then once in a while a fish would seemingly get bored with its enforced idleness, shoot upstream, make a sideways jump and splash back into the water again, returning to rest amongst its companions, who took no notice of this pointless burst of energy. All the symptoms of high noon in August on a Highland river.

Thinking about lunch, and maybe afterwards a sleep in the sunshine, like the salmon, we came to a pool called Maggie's Dip. Here the bank rises steeply on our side of the river, and it is impossible to use the conventional overhead cast to cover the water. It is not an easy pool to fish, but today it was in the shade, and to my mind offered a better chance than most. I said as much, and asked Jim Morrison if he would like to give the pool a try.

In some ways the switch or roll cast is not an elegant one to watch, until you see it being done expertly. The line is drawn up against the current, with some in hand ready to shoot, the rod remains upright slightly past the perpendicular where the forward drive would begin if you were casting normally, then switched suddenly down; the line coils out on the surface of the water, until the fly flips over and lands in a straight line from the tip of the rod. Jim Morrison showed how it was done. Phyllida and I watched as he fished down the pool, with no apparent result. 'When Jim's finished I'm going to try something,' she said.

By this time Morrison was nearing the end of the fishable water. Phyllida left me and headed for the neck of the pool. As she got to the bank her approach became cautious, like a cat stalking a mouse. Testing her foothold carefully, she waded in to the river where the current bounced evenly from bank to bank over the stony bottom, before becoming constricted to a sinuous glide of dark water as it entered the throat of the pool. I guessed now what she had in mind. I watched as she began to cast quite a short line then, slowly raising the rod point to the vertical, paused with the line hanging in a loop to the surface, before she cast again. I knew the fly would be cutting a vee on the surface, before it was flicked away for the next cast.

On a hot day with the river low, salmon will often lie right at the top of a pool, where the white water ends and the current proper begins, to get the benefit of the oxygen absorbed from the air by the shallow stream passing over the stones above. Whereas fish keeping to the depths for protection from the sun's rays can seldom be tempted from their lethargy, occasionally one which has chosen a lie at the top of the pool can; not to take with any enthusiasm, but more like a sunbather swatting at an insect to get rid of something annoying. Hence the reason for making one's fly as irritating as possible without actually scaring the salmon. The other practical difficulties are not to be seen by the fish, and any that do take an interest usually come short, miss the fly altogether, or are lightly hooked. Nevertheless, the thrill of anticipation as you watch the shape of a salmon materialise in the water, then roll porpoise-fashion to where your fly cuts its wake on the surface, goes a long way on a blank day.

By now Jim Morrison had come up to join me and we both watched Phyllida fishing. So far as she was concerned we might as well have been miles away, not yards. Her concentration was total. We could see only her cast, but both of us knew that she was watching that small wake on the surface for the dark shape that might swim up beneath it, then the white opening of the jaws that might or might not close on the fly. We saw her pause, then reel up and change the fly. She waited a good five minutes before casting again, just twice. Then we saw her rod bend, heard the tearing sound of line being stripped from the reel, and knew that the fly was taken. How long it would remain in place was another matter. Whatever happened it would not be a blank day for Phyllida Morrison.

I knew for certain now that both Jim and Phyllida Morrison were experienced in the art of salmon fishing.

That was the beginning of a friendship which went on for a fortnight. At the end of that time, which the Morrisons and ourselves spent fishing together, talking about it afterwards, laughing, putting the world to rights, and generally enjoying each other's company, they left us. We had a letter, dated the day following their departure, and headed with the address of a hotel in Northumberland, to which each of them had contributed their own way of saying how they had enjoyed themselves. It was a touching letter and I have it still. But we have never seen or heard from them since.

I told Tim Wedderburn when next he came to stay how much we had enjoyed having the Morrisons, and asked him to tell us something more about them because they had not said much about themselves.

'You did say Morrisons?' Tim replied, somewhat surprised, it struck me.

'Yes, Jim Morrison and his wife Phyllida.'

'Well you've certainly got the better of me,' exclaimed Tim, 'I've known Jim Morrison for years, he's a professor of something or another at London University, we meet occasionally but our paths don't often cross. Jim's wife died of cancer seven years ago; her name was Margaret, not Phyllida.'

How often have you heard someone say, 'I could write a book about that'. Yet when it comes to doing so they might find, as I have, that memory tumbles out at random, like pieces of a jigsaw puzzle emptied onto a table. But, like a jigsaw puzzle, some pieces are easier to find than others. So it has been with the people who have stayed with us over the years at Balmeanie; the faces recognised and the faces forgotten. There they all are, the remembered ones: Guy Lewis, Ernest Cantrell, the Cartwrights, the Morrisons, even Nigger, in the foreground; others less easily recognisable crowd around. Finding the right pieces for the background was more difficult. The picture I had in mind was never quite the same, a cloud there one morning gone the next, cataracts of white water running down the hillside today, just angry scars tomorrow; so many different memories of the same setting, and only these few coloured shapes to put in place.

There is no one staying now. That is how I have managed to complete these stories. I shall come down to breakfast tomorrow, there will be no guests at the table wanting to know my view on the fishing prospects, just Ann. Like many another well-adjusted man and wife, I will offer my sympathetic, 'Yes, darling, no, darling,' responses to her comments on the current domestic scene, smoothing the way for a return to reading the newspaper. Then I shall get up, make my way to the front porch, sniff the old goat's head to see whether it is going to be wet or dry, and then go outside to find out for myself. Either I will be able to see no further through the mist or slanting rain than the trees the other side of the river, or else to the westerly hills which look down on the Atlantic.

Despite what I have just read in yesterday's *Scotsman* (today's does not arrive until lunchtime) about the dangers of smoking, I shall light a cigarette, and depending on the state of the weather I shall go for my post-breakfast stroll without fear of interruption.

Breakfast over, and the preliminaries complete, I go outside. The sky is clear, the contours of the hills sharp against it; there is a chill in the air warning that winter is not far off. I get to wondering at the contrast between this vista and the real world I have just been reading about in the paper. Whose is the real world anyhow? This one I am looking at, created by God, or however else anyone likes to believe it was created, or the one I have been reading about, created by man? I do not know. My real world extends from here to Bettybridge with occasional forays further afield. I think of the people I have been writing about who have come from their own real worlds to visit mine, and I wonder if they got anything out of the experience.

The mind continues to ramble; strange what one keeps in store there, not just the important things but the bric-a-brac. One such item stored away in the corner, where it has been for the best part of forty years, is a film. It was not a famous film, I cannot remember the actors, only the title and the story. I have never noticed the name of the film again in print since the day I went to see it. But that film made an impression on me. Most people will not even have heard of the title. It was called *Halfway House*.

Now some mental gadgetry selects that stored-up slice of memory. Halfway House was a small country hotel buried deep in rural England. Each of the half-dozen or so guests staying there had some kind of personal problem: love, bereavement, money, self-respect gone, suicide just round the corner. I cannot remember the actual characters or their individual problems. But somehow the atmosphere of the hotel, and the relationships which developed between these strangers meeting for the first time there, helped each one of them to see their problems in perspective, and go back home

117

revitalised. That was the story, and it was not half as corny as I seem to have made it sound.

I think what must have appealed to me about that film was the happy ending. I am not one for being left in suspense to puzzle out some character's anguish. I like a nice, clean happy ending, though I appreciate in real life it does not often happen that way. Anyhow, the effect of this early soap was to make me think how places affect people. And I am sure they do.

Come on, Charles Rowley, pull yourself together. Stop being so introspective. You have finished writing about your guests, and anyway the idea was to write fishing stories about them, not indulge in fantasies.

Besides, there will be no more guests until next season, only family and friends to brave the north of Scotland in winter.

I really must stop dreaming, and think about some of the practical problems I should deal with. A moment later, as I watch an eagle drift high above the glen with a couple of effortless wing-beats to carry it from one side to the other, I am back to thinking about the effect which places have on people. What has Balmeanie had to offer besides the fishing? I think the same as Halfway House had to offer, escape. A tangled life stands more chance of being sorted out in the open than it does behind closed doors. Some of our guests may not have thought they were coming to a Halfway House when they came to stay, but when they left, I wonder...! Fishing was only part of the 'menu' − for some of them.

Good heavens, I have got carried away, I must go back and see what is happening in the real world, between here and Bettybridge.